# Eat Up Slim Down!

Annual Recipes ✱ 2012

# Eat Up Slim Down!

## Annual Recipes * 2012

200 Simply Delicious Recipes for Permanent Weight Loss

From the editors of **Prevention**.

RODALE.

*In all Rodale cookbooks, our mission is to provide delicious and nutritious recipes. Our recipes also meet the standards of the Rodale Test Kitchen for dependability, ease, practicality, and, most of all, great taste. To give us your comments, call (800) 848-4735.*

*Eat Up Slim Down* and *Prevention* are registered trademarks of Rodale Inc.

Printed in the United States of America
Rodale Inc. makes every effort to use acid-free ♾, recycled paper ♻.

Photo credits can be found on page 356.

ISBN-13   978–1–60961–791–2   hardcover

2   4   6   8   10   9   7   5   3   1   hardcover

 **RODALE.**

We inspire and enable people to improve their lives and the world around them.
For more of our products, visit **prevention.com** or call 800-848-4735.

## SPECIAL THANKS

We would like to thank all the readers of *Prevention* magazine and prevention.com for sharing clever tips and inspiring stories of their weight-loss success. You continue to inspire us to collect new and better recipes for *Eat Up Slim Down!* We salute you and wish you a lifetime of maintaining your new healthy weight.

And sincere, heartfelt thanks to the weight-loss winners who share their stories with us in personal profiles: Kate Chapman, Linda Kutenits, Reilin Harper, and Laura Wooster Baldwin.

A very special thank-you to everyone who had a hand in creating *Eat Up Slim Down! Annual Recipes 2012,* especially Carol Angstadt, JoAnn Brader, Hope Clarke, Anne Egan, Marielle Messing, and Sharon Sanders.

# Contents

# Introduction

**If your struggle to take off** excess pounds has you feeling down, you've picked up the right book. The weight-loss winners featured in *Eat Up Slim Down!* are the people you need to know right now! Broadway performer Kate Chapman and Reilen Harper, a working mother of triplet boys, are among those proud to say they are losers. They have collectively shed hundreds of pounds but gained so much more. Their spirits are soaring and they have energy to burn so they're sharing their stories and strategies for success.

Chapters 1 through 5 discuss the latest scientific discoveries and strategies for effective, long-term weight loss. In Lose Weight without Trying, you'll be motivated by the inspiring stories of four weight-loss winners who triumphed with the new "mindful eating" programs. Plus, we'll reveal Five Secrets of the Naturally Slim so you, too, will learn to think about and approach food differently. Weight-Loss Essentials outlines the basics to get you on track: Four Foods That Whittle Your Middle, 10 Simple Rules for Losing, and an essential personalized chart of how many meals you should eat each day. We also offer contingency plans for life's inevitable celebrations, ways to avoid diet disasters, and foods that will rev up your metabolism.

Recipes That Slim & Satisfy presents delectable dishes that fit easily into your busy life. More than 200 quick-and-easy recipes from *Prevention* magazine will get healthy meals on your table. Each one is kitchen tested for foolproof results. Also, there's no guessing about calories, carbs, fats, protein, and fiber. We've done the math so you don't have to. All you have to do is, well, eat up and slim down.

Start your day with a Double Tomato and Turkey Bacon Omelet or a Tutti-Frutti Smoothie. Lunch on a Better Beef Burger, Mushroom-Onion Pizza, or Wisconsin Cheese Chowder. For dinner, we've got you covered with family-friendly entrées such as Fettuccine and Meatballs, Creole Chicken and Sausage, and Baked Turkey Cutlets with Peppers and Mushrooms. An entire section on Snacks & Little Bites gives you fresh ideas for keeping hunger pangs at bay. How do Chipotle Bean Nachos, Strawberry Energizer Bars, and Crunchy Peanut Butter Cookies sound? And don't think we've forgotten about desserts. We have more than 45 of them—one irresistible choice after another. Dig into Lemon Pound Cake, Triple Chocolate Cheesecake, Apple Crumb Pie, Plum Strudel, and Strawberry Cream Clouds.

We'll tell you what you can prepare ahead of time. "Quick Tips" give you snippets of actionable information. "Nutrition News to Use" translates the latest scientific weight-loss breakthroughs into practical advice. For instance, do you know what nutrient can help flush saturated fat? Turn to page 106.

"Health Hearsays" provide expert answers to common health concerns. "Superfood Spotlight" guides you in purchasing the most nutritious ingredients. And Menus for Special Times reassures you that you can share good times with family and friends while still eating healthfully. Now that's something we can all celebrate!

# Lose Weight without Trying

**The latest weight-loss** breakthrough isn't a supplement, a pill, or an exotic berry. It's the human mind. Scientists and practitioners are discovering that for weight loss to be successful over the long term, it has to be about more than counting calories and crunches. It has to engage a dieter at the emotional level, too, because willpower is only partially a function of rational "will." To put "power" behind it, you need ways of combating the cycle of emotional and stress eating, which can sabotage the best intentions.

Across the country, from Florida to California, cutting-edge centers are practicing their own versions of this approach, because it simply works. Think of it this way: Diet and exercise are crucial—particularly, a healthy diet rich in fruits, vegetables, and fiber that can nourish the body and keep you feeling satisfied longer. But alone, diet and exercise are like a two-legged stool—ready to topple at the first snack attack. To steady the stool, you need a third leg—a stash of mind-body techniques to help you combat cravings and get in touch with your body's true needs.

What's more inspiring than weight-loss success? Share in the lessons learned by women who turned their lives around with the new "mindful eating" diet programs.

## AMY STEVENS

For Amy Stevens, 41, an IT manager and college instructor in women's studies from North Adams, Massachusetts, her grandmother's chocolate drop cookies always represented unconditional love. They reminded her of her grandma's warm, cozy kitchen and all the joy that surrounded her on birthdays, holidays, and those special afternoons when the two of them would bake together. So when a nutritionist suggested that Stevens give up the fudgy cookies (along with the fast food that made up the bulk of her diet), she sobbed for 15 minutes. But a year later, she hadn't baked a single batch—and she hadn't really missed them. She's managed to avoid the fast food too. She has dropped 80 pounds and is far happier than she was in the days when she turned for solace to oven-fresh cookies.

What changed Stevens's eating habits—and her life? A program called integrative weight loss at Kripalu Center for Yoga and Health in Stockbridge, Massachusetts. Kripalu coined the term *integrative weight loss* to refer to its holistic approach to slimming, yet the words *weight loss* are rarely mentioned during the center's 1-week sessions. Instead, the focus is on transforming the participants' relationships with food and the body through mindfulness, fitness walks, nutrition lectures, a share circle, yoga, yoga dance, deep breathing, and nutrition counseling, not to mention three meals a day of superhealthy fare.

For Stevens, it was an immersion course in healthy living.

These days, the married mother of two doesn't have time to think about cookies as she trains for—and competes in—triathlons. One was a team event in which she had to kayak 5 miles. "Two and a half miles into the kayaking, I was dying," she says. Then she looked up and saw Kripalu. (She was on the lake below it.) "From that moment on, I knew I could finish the race. It was one paddle in front of the other and making the right choice with every move," she says. "That's what Kripalu taught me."

### Make a Special Space for Meals

Too often we eat from a dining room table that's cluttered with newspapers and mail—if we sit down at the table at all. "I used to eat breakfast in the car out of a bag," says Stevens. Now she gets up early to eat in peace before the rest of the family rouses. She brings out her grandmother's good bone china plate and teacup. She gazes out her window over the peaceful Berkshire Mountains while slicing apples and brewing tea. "It's about as sacred a moment as I can create," she says. In such a mood, mindful eating comes much more naturally. And the serenity of the early morning sets the tone for a happier day, in which Stevens is more resilient against stress.

### Fight Fat by . . . Breathing?

At Kripalu, Stevens learned to quell cravings with deep breaths and meditation. "By the time I've focused on my

breath for 1 to 5 minutes, food is the last thing on my mind," she says. "Usually I realize it's not a real need." When her resolve does weaken, she no longer berates herself. She just tries to learn from her mistakes, so she doesn't repeat them. "At Kripalu, healthy living and eating are practice," says Stevens. "If you're only practicing, you can't fail."

### Find a Chorus of Affirming Voices

One of them for Stevens is the owner of a local restaurant called Stone Soup. The owner began creating special dishes for her that fit her post-Kripalu diet and were tasty, healthy, and inexpensive. (Stevens is a regular there.) These dishes proved so popular with other patrons that they're now on the menu. Family support has also been crucial for Stevens. "My husband has adapted with such grace and loving support, at times it takes my breath away," she says. He's read up on nutrition for her and searched out healthy recipes, both online and in used bookstores. He even helps cook, "and he makes sure I have fresh, local apples in my bowl every morning," she says. Even her 7- and 9-year-old children have joined in, without too much griping. "My daughter now claims Brussels sprouts with tofu is her favorite dish, and my son likes hummus," says Stevens. "Now when the kids are bad, I threaten to take them to McDonald's."

## SHERRI DE JESUS

As Sherri De Jesus waltzes across the dance floor in one of her flowing gowns, its seven-layered skirt swirls about her. Its sparkling bodice, which she helped design herself, is trimmed in more than 200 Swarovski crystals and adds to the glow of confidence she now feels. Five years ago, she could not have imagined taking up competitive dancing as a hobby. But here she is, dancing 4 nights a week and competing in ballroom, Latin, and swing. It never would have happened without a childhood enchantment with Fred Astaire, a lifelong desire to become a dancer—and mindful-eating training from the Pritikin Longevity Center + Spa in Miami.

Pritikin's reputation rests upon its renowned heart-health program—which has been documented through more than 100 studies in major medical journals—but participants also typically lose weight and reverse health markers related to diabetes and stroke. With Pritikin's training, De Jesus shed 72 pounds.

### Savor Your Food

Before attending the Pritikin program, 36-year-old De Jesus was in the early stages of a divorce—depressed, bored, and overeating. "Some people smoke to relieve stress," she says. "My thing was eating—chocolate cake, M&M's, candy bars. Sometimes I was so busy, I barely even noticed what I was chewing. There was no enjoyment in it."

All that has changed. Now she puts aside her work during meals and snacks and focuses instead on the flavors, textures, and aromas of her food—a practice known as mindful eating. The dual payoff is that she enjoys her food more and doesn't need as much to feel satisfied. At a party, if she indulges in a cookie, she'll take small bites and chew slowly. "Usually I don't actually finish the cookie because it's really sweet," she says. "Once you get in the habit of eating mindfully, a few bites go a long way."

### Stand Tall

De Jesus not only talks the talk, she now walks the walk—literally. At work as a hospital program director in Houston, she sits up straight at her desk and strides elegantly down halls. "I didn't know that if I held myself differently, my entire outlook on health would change," she says. It's a trick she learned at Pritikin in a class called Posture for Success. "By lengthening your spine and pulling back your shoulders, you instantly look better, as if you've taken weight off," she says. "You feel better about yourself, so people respond to you differently. They see you as someone who is sure of yourself and sure of the message you're presenting, which helps boost your self-confidence"—and, along with it, the ability to resist cravings.

### Follow Your Passion

It's not just good advice for life but great for weight loss, too. If you're engaged in activities you love, you're happier and less likely to need food for comfort. And if your hobby involves physical movement, such as a rumba or two-step, that's even better. "Experts warn you about the terrible things that will happen if you don't lose weight," De Jesus says. "But that fear lasts only so long before you go back to your normal way of living. On the other hand, if you find a positive goal that motivates you, you can stick with it. This isn't about dieting but creating a lifestyle."

## HOLLY SNYDER

A few years back, 45-year-old Holly Snyder's life was transformed—by paprika, along with cinnamon, ginger, garlic, and what she calls a serenade of herbs, spices, and fresh foods that she'd never known how to use until she attended a weight-loss program at Duke Integrative Medicine in her hometown of Durham, North Carolina. "When I was growing up, in my house, salt, pepper, and ketchup were vegetables," she says. But she began jazzing up salads with chickpeas, almond slivers, raisins, cranberries, and sunflower seeds. In the summer, she picks up sugar snap peas, vine-ripened tomatoes

from a friend's garden, locally grown strawberries, and juicy peaches at the farmer's market. "Lord, they're good," she says. "My mouth is watering just thinking about them." When she looks back on the food desert that used to constitute her diet, she says, "I feel so much more alive now." And she feels so much healthier since she's shed 25 pounds. "I've gone from barely making it once around a flat track to walking 5 kilometers in less than an hour, going up and down hills," she says. "If I can hike that trail on a 97-degree day, I can do anything I put my mind to."

### Weigh Your Values

Now when Snyder, an IT specialist, is tempted by Ben & Jerry's ("It's got to be a flavor with chocolate—I was born and raised in Hershey, Pennsylvania"), she pauses to think about what she truly values in life—namely, her family, friends, and health. This simple act helps break the normal flow from craving to snacking and gives her time to reflect on whether the temporary gratification is really what she wants for herself in the long run. (After all, it hasn't helped in the past.) "This technique doesn't always work," Snyder says. "But I've succeeded so many times that I've begun to realize I can do it. I have a new catchphrase for myself whenever I succeed:'Yay, me!'"

### It's Not All about the Pounds

At Duke, excess weight is seen as a symptom of underlying issues, such as low self-esteem. Duke offers two programs—a 3-day weekend class called Tip the Scales in Your Favor and an 8-week class at 90 minutes per week called Changing from Within. In both, mindful eating is a key to success. Extensive research at Duke has found that those who practice mindful eating not only feel more in control of their diet—they also improve their insulin sensitivity!

Snyder was taught to recognize what true hunger feels like. For 3 days, Duke asks participants to rate their hunger before, during, and after meals and snacks using

## 75%

Amount of
overeating that's
emotional
Source: Heartmath

a 7-point scale, where 1 is "very hungry" and 7 is "very full." Simple, right? Snyder found the exercise almost impossible at first. "In my perception, I was either full or starving," she says. But once she learned to separate sudden cravings from the creeping onset of hunger, she became better at resisting the urges. Equally impressive, she learned to recognize subtle physical cues that she was filling up, which enabled her to start saying no to seconds (and thirds). "Once you can consciously say you're not actually hungry anymore, you have less reason to keep eating," she says. "It blows my mind now how little food I really need to be satisfied."

### The Pen Is Mightier Than the Cookie

Journaling "felt stupid" to Snyder at first. But writing down exactly what she was eating—in addition to how she felt before and after each meal or snack—made her aware of just how much she was packing away every day. Soon she began cutting back. "I would think, 'Shoot, if I eat this, I'll have to write it in that damned journal,'" she says. Suddenly her beloved Ben & Jerry's was not something that eased stress but caused it. "It's neat to look at it from a different perspective," she says. "It's as if you're directing your own inner cinema and finding a script that's more in line with your goals."

### Silence Your Inner Critic

People with serious weight issues tend to judge themselves harshly, and Snyder was no exception. "Society looks at you differently when you're fat than when you're thin," she says. "You start looking at yourself that way, too. But at Duke, we did this exercise of trying to be still and forgive ourselves—for being fat, for making all these wrong choices, for the self-loathing that results." Most astonishing, she says, "I learned that I was worthy of good food and good health. That seems like a small thing, but for me it was life changing. Now eating is a choice, and I can trust myself to make the right decision. If I make mistakes, I forgive myself and start again." Clearly, it's working. "I lost 10 pounds in the first month without even consciously trying," she says. "Instead I just concentrate on how I feel—energy-wise

and health-wise—and the rest will fall into place. Experience is a powerful teacher, because it stays with you and touches that inner wisdom we all have."

## BEVERLY NICHOLS

When 52-year-old Beverly Nichols of Dallas goes to bed, she doesn't obsess over the day's stresses or the bad news on TV. Instead, she lies down and visualizes four angels—one at each of her hands and feet. "I've had nightmares for a long time," she says. But at Golden Door in Escondido, California, she learned how to drift into sleep by letting her angels stand guard. Banishing insomnia has been a key to keeping off that extra 10 pounds with which she struggled.

### Appreciate the Sounds of Silence

At Golden Door, Nichols, a married parent of four stepchildren, began learning tai chi, with its peaceful, silent

flow. "We're always so busy and have so much background noise," she says. "But when you're quiet, you'd be surprised how much you hear and smell and feel. Now I hike in silence instead of taking my iPod. It helps relax me. And the more stress I can take away from myself, the easier it is for me to control my weight."

The environment at Golden Door nurtured interior designer Snyder's appreciation of beauty and harmony. How stressed can you be while enjoying a setting that mimics a Japanese inn, with streams, waterfalls, and gardens filled with orange blossoms and wisteria—where the organic food comes straight from the spa's own garden? The customized program included early morning hikes, spa treatments, and classes such as yoga, biofeedback, and How to Get Happy.

### Nurture Gratitude

Before bed at night, Nichols writes down three things she's grateful for—"not generalities, like the kids or your health, but three specific events that happened that day, like a kind word from a colleague." It's called the Trio of Blessings exercise. "When you start looking for the positives, you realize how much you have to be grateful for," she says. "Serenity is about learning how to take care of yourself—how to be happy and focused and deal with difficult things that come up."

### Seek Friends with a Positive Outlook

"I will always have time for a true friend in trouble, but some people just drain your energy," Nichols says. She's gradually shed those friends and cultivated others who lift her spirits. "The last time I went to Golden Door, I didn't have any significant issues left," she says. "I went just for renewal. I have a much healthier life now."

## FIVE SECRETS OF THE NATURALLY SLIM

We all have that one slim friend—the one who's never bullied into submission by the bread basket, and when she says "I'll just have a bite," she does just that. Is she for real?

She is. Research shows that thin people simply don't think about food the same way that, well, the rest of us do. "Thin people have a relaxed relationship with food," explains David L. Katz, MD, professor of public health at Yale University. "Those who are overweight tend to be preoccupied by it. They focus on how much or how often they eat or attach labels like 'good' and 'bad' to certain foods. As a result, mealtime is always on the brain." Here, weight-loss experts explore the mysterious minds of the "naturally" slim. Act like you're a size smaller, and you will be a size smaller.

### 1 They're Satisfied, Not Stuffed

On a fullness scale of 1 to 10, the slim stop eating at 6 or 7, says Jill Fleming, RD, author of *Thin People Don't Clean Their Plates*. Others may go to 8 or 10. Why? Perhaps because some people equate fullness with satisfaction and feel deprived if they stop short, says Fleming. Or they may be used to finishing what's in front of them, regardless of whether they need or want it.

**Copy Them** Halfway through your next meal, put your fork down and, using the 1-to-10 scale, rate your level of fullness. Do it again when you have about five bites left. The goal is to increase your awareness of how satisfied you feel during a meal. Bonus: It also slows down your eating, which allows the sensation of fullness to settle in.

### 2 They Don't Use Food to Cure the Blues

It's not that thin women are immune to emotional eating, says Kara Gallagher, PhD, a weight-loss expert based in Louisville, but that they tend to recognize when they're doing it and stop.

**Copy Them** Add the word *HALT* to your vocabulary, says Dr. Gallagher. More than just a command (as in "stop eating that entire sleeve of cookies"), it's an acronym that stands for "hungry, angry, lonely, or tired"—the four most common triggers for emotional eating. If you're truly hungry, choose a balanced snack, such as a handful of nuts, to tide you over until your next meal. But if you're angry, lonely, or tired, seek an alternative, calorie-free solution to your emotional need. Blow off steam by going for a run or just

jumping around—the heartbeat boost will help dissipate your anger. Lonely? Call a friend, e-mail your kid, or walk to the park or mall. Being around others will make you feel more connected to your community, even if you don't bump into anyone you know. If you're tired, for heaven's sake, sleep!

### 3 They Have a Self-Control Gene

Tufts University researchers found that the biggest predictor of weight gain for women in their fifties and sixties was their level of disinhibition, or unrestrained behavior. Women with low disinhibition (that is, a finely tuned sense of restraint) had the lowest body mass index. High disinhibition (i.e., low restraint) was linked to adult weight gain of up to 33 pounds.

**Copy Them** Prepare for moments when disinhibition is higher—such as a festive atmosphere or when you're with a large group of friends. At a party, tell yourself you'll take one of every fourth passed hors d'oeuvre. If you're out to dinner, order an appetizer portion and share dessert. And when you're stressed—another low-restraint moment—make sure you have healthy snacks such as fruit or carrot sticks on hand.

### 4 They're Movers and Shakers

On average, slender people are on their feet an extra 2½ hours per day—which can help burn off 33 pounds a year, according to a study from the Mayo Clinic in Rochester, Minnesota.

**Copy Them** Try a reality check. Studies have shown that people often overestimate how active they really are, says Dr. Gallagher. Most people actually spend 16 to 20 hours a day just sitting or being still. Wear a pedometer on a typical day to see how close you get to the recommended 10,000 steps. Your day should combine 30 minutes of structured exercise with a variety of healthy habits, such as mopping the floor with extra vigor or taking the stairs instead of the elevator. To find out how many calories your activities burn, see the exercise calculator at www.caloriecontrol.org.

## 5 They Sleep—Well

It takes only 1 night of sleep deprivation to increase levels of hunger-triggering ghrelin and decrease levels of hunger-suppressing leptin. As a result, your body thinks you're starving, which spikes cravings for high-fat and high-calorie foods, says Ann E. Rogers, PhD, RN, associate professor at the University of Pennsylvania School of Nursing in Philadelphia.

Slim people snooze 2 more hours per week, compared with overweight people, says a study from Eastern Virginia Medical School in Norfolk. Researchers theorize that a lack of shut-eye is linked to lower levels of appetite-suppressing hormones such as leptin and higher levels of the appetite-boosting hormone ghrelin.

**Copy Them** Break it down: Two extra hours of sleep a week is only 17 more minutes a day—manageable for even the most packed schedules. Start there and slowly work toward 8 hours of snooze time a night—the right amount for most adults.

What could be easier than literally losing weight while you sleep? It sounds like a dream come true. Practice heading off to dreamland a few minutes earlier every night. Unwind 1 hour before bedtime by reading or meditating.

## CUT YOUR CRAVINGS

A regular yoga routine can help you drop a dress size. People who practice yoga are more likely to eat mindfully—noshing only when physically hungry and stopping when full, reports a study from the Fred Hutchinson Cancer Research Center in Seattle. That may be why they also weigh about 15 pounds less than people who don't do yoga. Researchers believe that yoga cultivates an awareness of emotional and physical sensations, increasing consciousness of food choices.

## MUSCLE YOUR WAY TO MORE WILLPOWER

Next time a cupcake calls to you from a bakery window, make a fist and keep walking. Clenching any of your muscles increases willpower—it's like a mental metaphor for resisting temptation, says Aparna Labroo, PhD, of the University of Chicago, the author of a new study involving self-control issues and accepting immediate pain for long-term gain. Health-conscious people who tightened a muscle while selecting food from a snack

# ✱ MIND OVER MIDSECTION

Studies suggest that focus and imagination may boost the proven power of diet and exercise.

**Keep Your Eyes on the Fries**
People who ate lunch while playing a computer game felt less full than those who dined without distractions, according to a new study from the University of Bristol in England.

**Contemplate the Possibilities**
Study subjects ate less cheese after they first visualized themselves eating the treat for 1½ minutes, according to scientists at Carnegie Mellon University in Pittsburgh. Repeatedly imagining the experience diminishes the craving for that food, the researchers speculate.

**Stage a Photo Finish**
Tracking calories can be a potent way of reminding yourself just how much you're eating. Better yet: Take a picture. Dieters who photographed everything they consumed were able to reflect on what they were going to eat and make healthier choices, reports a study from the University of Wisconsin–Madison.

# ✳ DOWN-DOGGING INTO A SIZE 6

Most traditional forms of yoga burn only 200 calories or so per hour, so consider intensifying your workout by mixing in some cardio or trying a more difficult class. Below are caloric breakdowns (based on a 140-pound woman) for various types of yoga.

### Hatha

A gentle form that focuses on basic postures and breathing techniques

**The burn:** 175 calories per hour

**Same as:** a slow walk

### Vinyasa

More intense than Hatha, with poses linked together in a fast, flowing sequence

**The burn:** 445 calories per hour

**Same as:** an hour of moderate bike riding

### Power Yoga

Similar to Vinyasa

**The burn:** 300 calories per hour

**Same as:** a brisk walk

### Bikram and Hot Yoga

Class comprises 26 postures performed in a studio heated to higher than 100°F

**The burn:** 636 calories per hour

**Same as:** an hour of jogging

bar were more likely to pass up decadent treats and opt for good-for-you fruit. Caveats: You have to be focused on healthy eating, and you have to clench the muscle while facing the dilemma.

## MIDDLE MANAGEMENT

Yoga is a known stress buster, but it's also one of the most effective workouts for fighting stubborn fat stores. Studies show that it lowers levels of stress hormones and increases insulin sensitivity—a signal to your body to burn food as fuel rather than store it as fat.

### Stress Less—Binge Less

Stress is not just bad for your mental state—it can also trigger the body to release excessive amounts of cortisol, the "cravings" hormone that makes you reach for comfort foods that are high in fat and sugar. A yoga routine could help you control both emotions and cravings.

"Yoga not only reduces stress, but it may also help lessen emotional eating," says Bruce W. Smith, PhD, assistant professor of psychology at the University of New Mexico in Albuquerque. His preliminary study found that yoga diminished binge eating by 51 percent, with participants losing an average of 6 pounds in 8 weeks. It may also help on a biochemical level. Researchers at Jefferson Medical College drew blood samples from 16 yoga novices and found that cortisol levels dropped by about 15 to 20 percent as early as day 1.

## STOP CRAVINGS WITH THIS YOGA TECHNIQUE

Though we can't create anxiety-free lives for ourselves, we can do something about the stress that can lead to impulse eating. "There's no question: Yoga practiced appropriately will have an impact on relaxing the mind," says Lorenzo Cohen, PhD, professor in the department of behavioral science and director of the integrative medicine program at the University of Texas M.D. Anderson Cancer Center in Houston.

Call it a margarita-mantra. When you're out with friends—and craving another drink or bite—rather than try to banish the craving, make like a yogi and focus on it. "Our tendency is to push away a craving, but then it gets really big and you are fighting with the craving. It becomes a major drama," says Cyndi Lee, founder of OM Yoga in New York City. Rather, a yogic way of dealing with the urge is to admit that you are having the craving and observe it. Notice the response in your body to what is happening at that moment. Continue observing your urge to indulge and it will change, Lee advises. "Eventually, the response is more fascinating than the craving."

[ it worked for me ]

# 100 pounds lost!

## ✳ KATE CHAPMAN

Actress-singer Kate Chapman used to get only the "fat lady" parts. Now that she's half her former size, she's taking Broadway by storm.

### My Story

From the time I first took the stage in a production of *The Sound of Music* when I was in elementary school, I knew I wanted to be on Broadway. I didn't actually move to New York until I was 21, and by then I was 20 pounds overweight. I went out for roles but received the same rejection time and time again: "Your physique doesn't match your voice."

As a soprano who can belt out the chesty, powerful sound that Broadway musical directors want, I sang for shows like *Saturday Night Fever, Dreamgirls,* and *Hair,* but always for recordings or from the orchestra pit. Finally, after 10 years, during which I gained 60 more pounds, I was cast in the Radio City Christmas Spectacular. I was so happy to be onstage, it didn't matter that I was playing the pleasantly plump Mrs. Claus. That led to my being cast in more big-woman roles. My Broadway dreams had come true—just not as a leading lady.

## VITAL STATS

Pounds lost: 100
Age: 40
Height: 5'4"
Weight then: 225 pounds
Weight now: 125 pounds

In 2004, I married a man with two sons I adored. When I noticed that the 6-year-old was gaining weight, I started taking him to the park to play. One day, when he was struggling on the monkey bars, he asked me to show him how it was done. I was horrified when I couldn't swing across three rungs without dropping. At that moment I heard a voice in my head say, "You can't help him if you can't help yourself." I knew I had to change my sedentary, quesadilla-and-McDonald's-filled lifestyle.

I started to revamp my habits—swapping unhealthy foods for better choices, adding activity to each day, and walking at least 30 minutes a day. Within 6 months, I had lost 55 pounds, trimmed 14 inches from my waist, and had my costume altered three times!

I had a role in *Mary Poppins* when I hit my dream weight of 130 pounds. Since I no longer looked like my character, I was cut from the show—but not for long. In a few months, I was recast, playing a much more energetic character. Since then I've understudied seven different roles in the show and can dance in longer numbers. I've also played Eva Perón in *Evita*—a dream come true. Now I regularly audition for the leading lady or pretty vixen, and my goal is to play Donna in *Mamma Mia.* I think I'd be great!

## My Top Tips

* Savor the taste of food . . . Take joy in eating instead of eating for emotional comfort.

* Ditch processed foods . . . I soon developed a taste for fruits, veggies, and whole grains.

* Focus on your motivation . . . When I couldn't keep up with my 6-year-old stepson at the playground, I realized I needed to reinvent myself—for both of us.

* Build movement into regular activities . . . Promising myself that I would run up the stairs that went from the basement dressing room to the stage really added up because I changed 17 times each night.

* Negotiate around obstacles . . . When cast in a show, the contract forbids you to change your physical appearance unless the executives approve. I was playing an older woman in *Les Misérables,* and I was nervous about asking for permission to lose weight. They agreed, on one condition: They would take my costumes in but would not take them out!

# Weight-Loss Essentials

**Chock it up to the child** within us all: When we decide to lose weight, we want to lose it *right now!* Since it took more than a few days to gain those 10, 20, or more pounds, is slashing calories a realistic (not to mention healthy) option? Nutrition experts recommend that you don't dip below 1,200 to 1,500 calories a day. "If you crash diet for more than 2 weeks or so, your metabolism will temporarily slow down," says George L. Blackburn, MD, PhD, associate director of the division of nutrition at Harvard Medical School. "So the same exact dieting effort results in less and less weight loss." Your body starts conserving energy, and you lose muscle along with fat. This can slow down your metabolism, even long after your crash diet is done. "If you want to drop 10 pounds, get started 10 weeks before your goal, not 4," says Dr. Blackburn. "You'll have a better chance of actually taking off the weight permanently." Aim to shed about a pound a week by shaving 250 calories and burning an extra 250 calories each day. Diet fads come and go, but slow and steady wins the weight-loss race.

## BEST SNACK PAIRS FOR WEIGHT LOSS

If cravings kill your diet, kill your cravings instead with hunger-busting snacks, suggests Tanya Zuckerbrot, RD. In a 4-week survey, she found that women who munched on a combination of protein, fiber, and healthy fats felt more satisfied and had less of an urge to overeat. Fiber increases satiety, and protein and fats digest slowly, delaying hunger. Here are some of Zuckerbrot's favorite combos—and they're only 150 calories each.

> ½ cup fiber-rich cereal + 1 serving 0% Greek yogurt

> 2 cups popcorn + 2 tablespoons trail mix

> 1 ounce baked potato chips + 2 tablespoons bean dip

# ✱ HOW MANY MEALS SHOULD I EAT?

Research has shown that eating meals of about 400 calories each provides a varied diet and keeps hunger at bay till the next time you eat. To reach your goal, consult the chart below and find your activity level to determine how much you should be eating every day.

**Sedentary:** You sit most of the day and drive everywhere, and you log plenty of hours of screen time each day.

**Somewhat active:** You get about 30 minutes of nonstrenuous physical activity daily—generally, the equivalent of walking about 1½ to 3 miles, or 3,000 to 6,000 steps.

**Active:** You like to move and get 30 to 60 minutes of daily activity by hitting the gym, climbing stairs, and running errands on foot or bike—the equivalent of walking more than 3 miles per day, or more than 6,000 steps.

**Very active:** You thrive on high-intensity sports and rigorous activities that total more than 60 minutes per day.

### WOMEN

| ACTIVITY LEVEL | TO LOSE | TO MAINTAIN |
| --- | --- | --- |
| Sedentary | 3 meals | 3–4 meals |
| Somewhat active/active | 3–4 meals | 4 meals |
| Very active | 4 meals | 4–5 meals |

### MEN

| ACTIVITY LEVEL | TO LOSE | TO MAINTAIN |
| --- | --- | --- |
| Sedentary | 3–4 meals | 4 meals |
| Somewhat active/active | 4 meals | 4–5 meals |
| Very active | 4–5 meals | 5+ meals |

# FOUR FOODS THAT WHITTLE YOUR MIDDLE

### Whole Grains
The *American Journal of Clinical Nutrition* found that dieters who ate five servings of whole grains daily for 12 weeks lost twice as much belly fat as those who ate refined carbs. The study credits the higher fiber in whole grains for the subjects' reduction in abdominal fat.

### Blueberries
Overweight rats fed the equivalent of 1 cup of blueberries a day stored less belly fat than those that didn't eat them, a University of Michigan study found. Researchers believe compounds in the pigment that gives blueberries their tint may activate genes related to fat burning.

### Green Tea
Study participants who drank up to 5 cups of green tea daily had greater exercise-induced declines in ab flab than non–tea drinkers, finds research in the *Journal of Nutrition*. Study authors think that green tea may stimulate the body's fight-or-flight response, altering fat storage.

### Dried Fruit
Munching on 2 tablespoons of dried fruit per day may help stave off belly fat, according to an analysis of the National Health and Nutrition Examination Survey. Measure out $1/8$ cup and toss into oatmeal, trail mix, salad, or grain dishes for a burst of sweetness.

# 10 SIMPLE RULES FOR LOSING

When it comes to weight loss, traditional strategies work. Obese adults who were given 10 basic rules were motivated enough to lose 4 pounds in 8 weeks. Follow the rules and you could cut up to 900 calories a day, study authors say—enough to lose nearly 15 pounds in 2 months.

> Eat your meals on a regular schedule.
> Choose low-fat foods.

> Wear a pedometer and walk 10,000 steps a day.

> Pack healthy snacks.

> Check the fat and sugar content on food labels.

> Portion wisely and skip seconds (except vegetables).

> Stand for 10 minutes every hour.

> Avoid sugary drinks.

> Turn off the television while you eat.

> Eat at least five servings of fruits and veggies daily.

nutritionist Cynthia Sass, MPH, RD, the author of *Cinch! Conquer Cravings, Drop Pounds, and Lose Inches*. *Prevention*'s cool and useful tool at www.prevention.com/mealbalancer gives you fast fixes to upgrade 15 of your favorite meals, including sandwiches, burritos, and even party spreads.

**Try it out:** Click on a slice of pizza and follow the tips—add more veggies, use less cheese, and leave the end crust behind—to save 85 calories. Before you know it, you'll be back at your fighting weight!

## SLIMMING SCIENCE

Keeping dirty dishes or empty glasses in view can help control overeating. When researchers at Cornell University in Ithaca, New York, treated students to a free buffet, those whose dishes piled up ate 28 percent less than people whose tables were continually bused. The people who ate more thought they were hungrier, because they didn't have a visual cue to keep their appetites in check. "You'll eat less if you see evidence of what you've already eaten," says Brian Wansink, PhD, director of Cornell's Food and Brand Lab and author of *Mindless Eating*.

## GOAL: DROP A SIZE IN ONE STEP

If you're still struggling with unwanted pounds, follow this simple rule to lose them for good: Fill half your plate with fruits and veggies and the other half with equal parts whole grains and lean protein. "You'll cut up to 30 percent of calories with this simple change," says

## ✱ GOTTA TRY IT: INSTANT MOTIVATOR

Frustrated by a stuck scale? The Fitbit (www.fitbit.com) picks up movements, from standing to running, and counts calories to spur you to move more and burn extra fat. Seeing the numbers add up motivated our tester to melt 2,439 calories in 1 day—without doing an actual workout.

## RESIST MENU WORDS THAT PACK POUNDS

Mouthwatering descriptions can suggest that an unhealthy dish is worth the splurge—when it's just the same old grub you'd get anywhere, warns Dr. Wansink. Some red flags:

### Kansas City barbecue
We assume regional food tastes better, even if the restaurant isn't in the referenced locale.

### Velvety chocolate mousse
Sensory words like *creamy, juicy,* and *triple-rich* induce cravings, even though items without such labels taste the same.

### Grandma's homemade apple pie
We have positive associations with certain means of preparation—think homemade or traditional—that encourage us to order foods prepared that way.

### Jack Daniel's glazed ribs
If you like a specific brand, you think you'll like menu items featuring its flavor.

## START ROUGHING IT

It's no secret that fiber is essential, possibly reducing the risk of heart disease and diabetes, as well as helping us keep our appetites—and waistlines—in check. The mystery seems to be how to get enough of it. Most women consume only half the recommended 21 to 25 grams daily. Try these six options for something jazzier than brown rice.

### Spike smoothies with chocolate.
A tablespoon of unsweetened cocoa powder has 2 grams of fiber, plus it contains less saturated fat than dark chocolate bars and none of the added sugars.

### Toss mushrooms into soup.
Rehydrate dried shiitakes in hot water for 20 to 30 minutes, then chop and add them to your favorite soup for

## ✻ STOP A CRAVING IN 5-4-3-2-1!

✻ Name 5 things you see in front of you.

✻ Identify 4 colors you see.

✻ Describe 3 things your body is feeling (such as temperature or a texture, like your shirt fabric).

✻ Identify 2 sounds.

✻ State 1 thing that you can smell.

### Why It Works
"Focusing on your senses quiets the chatter in your mind so you can tune in to your body's signals better—and decide whether you're really hungry," says psychologist Susan Albers, PsyD, author of *50 Ways to Soothe Yourself without Food.*

3 grams of fiber per ounce, plus lentinan, a compound that may have anticancer properties.

### Add edamame to stir-fries.

Brimming with folate, a B vitamin that may protect women from pancreatic cancer, and 4 grams of fiber per ½ cup, boiled green soybeans—called edamame in Japan—complement any Asian flavor.

### Make pumpkin-pie oatmeal.

Combine ⅓ cup canned pumpkin, 1 cup cooked oatmeal, 1 to 2 teaspoons brown sugar, and spices of your choice, such as cinnamon, nutmeg, or pumpkin pie spice. The pumpkin adds nearly 2.5 grams of fiber and loads of immunity-boosting vitamin A.

### Sprinkle wheat germ into pancakes.

Rich in selenium, which could cut skin cancer incidence by about 60 percent, ½ cup of wheat germ packs 4 grams of fiber. Add it to any batter recipe.

### Mix oats into meat loaf.

Instead of nutritionally inferior bread crumbs, use ⅔ cup rolled oats per pound of meat as a binding agent. In addition to 5.5 grams of fiber, they contain magnesium, a mineral that may slash diabetes risk.

# FIVE NUTRIENTS TO BOLSTER HEALTHY WEIGHT LOSS

Successful and healthy long-term weight loss is about much more than fitting into that little black dress for your class reunion. Taking in fewer calories is part of the equation, but unless we nourish our bodies with essential nutrients, we won't maintain the vigor, stamina, disease resistance, and metabolic efficiency that's needed to succeed long term. Even if you're diligent about your diet, you're likely to fall short on five critical nutrients, according to recent USDA figures on the average amounts most midlife women consume. And with headlines questioning the value of multivitamins, it's even more important to make up the difference with tasty, readily available foods, says Lisa Hark, PhD, RD, a family-nutrition expert based in Philadelphia.

Simple changes to your diet can provide a powerful defense against disease and bolster your healthy weight goal. "With food, you're getting not just isolated nutrients, as you might in a supplement, but a full range of them in the form nature intended," says Dr. Hark, a coauthor of *Nutrition for Life*.

Here is where you may fall short—and how you can measure up.

## Vitamin E
**You need:** 15 milligrams/day
**You probably get:** 6.4 milligrams/day
**Your shortfall:** 57 percent
This powerful antioxidant protects your cells, helps them communicate with each other, and defends your skin against UV damage. If you don't get enough vitamin E, you may have problems absorbing other nutrients.

**HELP MAKE IT UP**
*(Choose two or three daily)*

> **¼ cup dry roasted sunflower seeds:** Munch on a handful or toss them on salads.

> **¼ cup wheat germ:** Sprinkle into yogurt.

> **1 tablespoon vegetable oil:** Use instead of butter to sauté kale, Swiss chard, or other leafy greens.

> **1 cup red bell pepper:** Chop and simmer in pasta sauce.

> **1 cup low-sodium canned white beans:** Mash with spices and use as a dip with celery sticks.

## Potassium
**You need:** 4,700 milligrams/day
**You probably get:** 2,458 milligrams/day
**Your shortfall:** 48 percent
This electrolyte keeps your nervous system humming and your muscles toned. It also helps keep your blood pressure at normal levels. If you don't get enough, you may feel irritable, weak, and fatigued. To avoid this, you must eat enough potassium-rich foods and control sodium. That's because the two minerals need to be balanced in your body, and either too little potassium or too much sodium (which is often found in excess in packaged foods) can cause problems.

**HELP MAKE IT UP**
*(Pick three or four daily)*

> **1 medium baked potato, with skin:** Top with salsa or chopped chives for a low-fat side dish.

> **1 cup edamame:** Steam with snow peas and corn kernels; let cool slightly, and then toss with dressing for a quick warm salad.

> **1 cup cooked spinach:** Add to a pasta dish.

> **1 cup cooked lentils:** Have a bowl of low-sodium lentil soup.

> **1 cup sliced banana:** Use a blender to whir into smoothies.

### Vitamin A
**You need:** 700 micrograms/day
**You probably get:** 558 micrograms/day
**Your shortfall:** 20 percent
This nutrient powers your eyesight, especially your night vision, and keeps your skin, gums, and teeth healthy. It also boosts your immune system and helps you fight off viruses. The older you get, the more you seem to require it to protect cognitive function. A study at Utah State University in Logan found that older adults with high intakes of antioxidants, including beta-carotene (from which your body makes vitamin A), had a slower rate of mental decline.

**HELP MAKE IT UP**
*(Have one or two daily)*

> **1 small sweet potato:** Baked, it's a flavorful, brightly hued side dish.

> **¼ cup canned pumpkin:** Use along with a dash of cinnamon to jazz up whole wheat pancake batter.

> **10 medium baby carrots:** Use as dippers for hummus.

> **1 cup cantaloupe cubes:** Dollop with reduced-fat cottage cheese and drizzle with honey.

> **½ cup dried apricots:** Chop and sprinkle on muesli.

### Calcium
**You need:** 1,000 to 1,200 milligrams/day
**You probably get:** 800 milligrams/day
**Your shortfall:** 20 to 33 percent
This mighty mineral builds strong bones, and that means a lower risk of osteoporosis for you. Calcium can help prevent some other major diseases as well. In a study of nearly 84,000 women by Tufts Medical Center in Boston, scientists found that those who consumed at least 1,200 milligrams of calcium daily (along with at least 800 IU of vitamin D, which helps absorption of the mineral) had a 33 percent lower risk of developing type 2 diabetes.

**HELP MAKE IT UP**
*(Choose three or four daily)*

> **8 ounces low-fat plain yogurt:** For dessert, pair it with fresh or thawed frozen berries and garnish with fresh mint.

> **3 ounces canned sardines with bones:** Quarter the sardines while they're still in the can. Toss with chopped fresh tomatoes and salad dressing, and serve over mesclun mix.

> **1 ounce low-fat cheese:** Grate some reduced-fat Parmesan into risotto, or use it to top pasta.

> **½ cup tofu:** Stir-fry with veggies.

> **1 cup cooked chopped bok choy:** Warm in broth for a calcium-rich soup.

**Magnesium**

**You need:** 320 milligrams/day
**You probably get:** 267 milligrams/day
**Your shortfall:** 17 percent

Magnesium is used in hundreds of chemical activities in the body, ranging from storing energy to helping your genes function properly. It keeps your nerves and muscles toned, your bones strong, and your blood circulating steadily. This mineral is so influential that women who got at least the recommended amount cut their risk of metabolic syndrome by 38 percent or more, reported a study by the Centers for Disease Control and Prevention. The serious, increasingly common syndrome, affecting some 50 million Americans, is a constellation of risk factors for heart disease and diabetes that includes excess abdominal fat, high blood pressure, and more.

**HELP MAKE IT UP**

*(Get three or four daily)*

> **1 cup cooked black beans:** Toss into a salad, along with chopped cilantro.
> **1 ounce (6 to 8 whole) Brazil nuts:** Chop and sprinkle on breakfast cereal.
> **1 cup okra:** Simmer fresh or frozen chopped okra in chicken soup or stew.
> **1 cup cooked brown rice:** Use as an accompaniment to a stir-fry.
> **1 ounce almonds:** Toast slivered almonds for a minute in a skillet over low heat, then sprinkle on fruit salad.

# ✳ 5 WAYS TO EAT LESS

✳ **Plate your main course in the kitchen.** Keep your entrée, starches, and high-fat foods in the kitchen. Keeping them off the table allows you to linger over conversation without temptation. Do put plain veggies, salad, or the fruit you're having for dessert on the table.

✳ **Don't jump up to clear the dishes.** In one study, volunteers ate 30 percent more chicken wings when the bones were whisked off the table than when the evidence was left to pile up in plain view. If you're having muffins baked in muffin papers, cookies from a box, ice cream, or any other high-cal food that creates trash, leave the debris out while you nosh so you'll be aware of how much you ate.

✳ **Use smaller plates and tall, skinny glasses.** Buck the trend toward dinnerware fit for a giant. A normal-sized portion looks ample on a slightly smaller plate. And several studies show that everyone from kids to longtime bartenders pour less when they're using tall, skinny glasses than when using wide, squat ones.

✳ **Stop, look, and listen while you eat.** Don't talk with your mouth full. Cultivate the art of conversation and prolong your meal by putting your fork down between bites and focusing on table talk. Some couples and families share positive experiences from their day with each other at mealtime. (And turn off the TV during meals!)

✳ **Don't miss meals.** Skipping needed food during the day can leave you authentically hungry at night, when your resistance is lower because you're tired. If you don't have time for breakfast, settle on one or two morning meals to eat on the run or set up the night before. If you find yourself skipping an afternoon snack, bring one from home so that it becomes a no-brainer.

[ it worked for me ]

# 138 pounds lost!

## LINDA KUTENITS

She was once so out of shape that just sitting still left her breathless. Now she's 138 pounds lighter. Here's how she got her life back.

### My Story

I grew up in an old-school Italian family in which cheese-smothered foods like pizza and baked ziti ruled the dinner table—and I never understood the meaning of *full*. I was a chubby child, an overweight teen, and an obese adult. At 36 I was 268 pounds, but worse, as my kids loaded up on junk food under my watch, I knew my overeating was setting a poor example. I remember the night it hit me. I was at our favorite diner—feeling out of breath but still ready to dig into my jumbo cheeseburger—when I realized this latest high-calorie indulgence would just make me feel worse. I had to change.

I quartered my portions, read about nutrition, cooked for my family (good-bye, greasy diner), and wrung calories from every one of my favorite childhood meals. If it called for whole milk, I'd use fat-free. I replaced butter with applesauce in desserts. For taste, I went crazy with spices—garlic and fresh herbs

## VITAL STATS

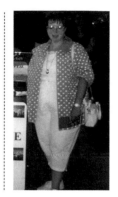

Pounds lost: 138

Age: 47

Height: 5'1"

Weight then: 268 pounds

Weight now: 130 pounds

galore. It was trial and error at first, but now I'm a pro. When I feed big groups, no one is the wiser that everything is half the calories!

I started moving—when I cooked, I'd play music and dance around my kitchen. I was too embarrassed to work out in public, but as pounds came off, I grew confident and started walking with friends. Six months later and 75 pounds lighter, I joined a gym. Now I exercise 5 days a week but move all 7.

My proudest achievement? My boys are equipped with the knowledge to make healthy decisions for the rest of their lives. I'm no longer the McDonald's mom. I've created a lifestyle that's not going to change.

I'm training to join a bike club. Recently, a group passed me by. I tried to keep up, but I wasn't quite there. I'm working to amp up my speed and endurance.

## My Top Cooking Tips

* Pizza . . . On flatbread, sprinkle low-fat cheese and top with leftover grilled veggies.

* Baked ziti . . . Opt for ricotta and mozzarella made from fat-free instead of whole milk. Simmer fresh herbs, garlic, and mushrooms—not fatty meats—in sauce to add flavor.

* Meatballs . . . Use a lean beef or even ground turkey in 90 percent of the meatball, and use just 10 percent fattier meat. Load up on spices and toss into the oven (not the deep fryer).

* Tiramisu . . . Try fat-free cream cheese and halve it, swapping the rest with light devil's food pudding. Use egg substitute, not eggs, and make sure the milk is fat free. Layer with light ladyfingers.

* Eggplant Parmesan . . . Skip the eggs—dip in fat-free milk instead. Go easy on whole wheat bread crumbs, and bake, don't fry. Top with low-fat cheese.

# Live Life, Lose Weight

**That second visit** to the all-you-can-eat buffet table, an extra sliver of birthday cake, a few days of restaurant meals on a business trip, some cocktails with friends after a tough week at the office . . . By themselves, each of those splurges seems so innocent. But like most things in life, dietary indulgences come at a cost. Most of us never lose the 1 to 2 pounds we gain every year between Thanksgiving and New Year's Eve—and over the years, they add up. Now multiply those pounds by all the other derail-your-diet occasions that life throws at you. The damage can be even worse when hearty eating patterns take hold and last well beyond the initial overindulgence. But when you have a contingency plan, your diet won't be thrown off track by the predictable variables of daily life. Temporary weight gain from holidays, vacations, family reunions, office parties, and business trips will be just that—temporary. The following guide will show you how to live your life and love your weight!

# THE 3-DAY RECOVERY PLAN

Think of this plan as your healthy-weight-maintenance insurance policy. Whenever you've gotten into an "anything goes" mode, this easy-to-follow program will get you back on track fast, with no guesswork on your part. It's simple and effective. Stick with it and you'll shed those extra pounds pronto.

### Break the Cycle
### The Splurge
There's no getting around it—our culture equates good times with sweet tastes. From birthday cake to Thanksgiving pumpkin pie, we can face a nightmare brought on by too many sweet treats. While experts used to dismiss the notion of sugar addiction, a growing body of research suggests that the sweet stuff can hijack the same brain circuitry that's affected by drugs and alcohol, leading to a vicious cycle of cravings and binges. And desserts with hefty amounts of both sugar and fat pack a double whammy. The sugar hooks you, while the fat piles on the pounds.

### The Solution
Eliminate desserts that are rich in sugar and fat for at least 3 days—7 to 10 would be even better. This will help quell cravings while you start to reestablish a taste for naturally sweet foods, such as fruit and starchy vegetables.

### Resize Your Belly
### The Splurge
As the "it's a vacation—I'll diet next week" mentality sets in, one of your natural appetite-control systems—the stomach's network of stretch receptors—starts losing its effectiveness. Normally, when your stomach is full, these receptors send messages to the brain that say "I'm satisfied." But prolonged periods of overeating make the receptors less sensitive. This helps explain why that feeling of "I'm so full, I'll never eat again" is followed the next day by the sense that you're even hungrier than usual.

### The Solution
If you keep eating the same high-calorie foods but merely reduce the quantity, your stretch receptors will signal your brain that you're starving and need emergency rations—

now. You can short-circuit this by eating healthy-size servings of low-calorie, high-fiber foods such as fruits, vegetables, and whole grains. Their bulk will keep the receptors happy while avoiding excess calories.

### Cut Down on Cocktails
### The Splurge
So you joined in a few too many toasts at your neighbor's going-away party? Alcohol packs in 7 calories per gram (compared with 4 for protein and carbs and 9 for fat). And the stomach and brain don't register liquid calories in the same way they do solids, so it's easy to go right on eating and drinking—without compensating for the added calories.

### The Solution
Satisfying, low-calorie beverages can boost metabolism and even temper hunger. Tea (lose the cream and sugar) has zero calories and lifts metabolic rate. Or prepare a pitcher of flavored water. Add sliced oranges, lemons, and limes to a pitcher, or toss in berries or sprigs of mint or lemongrass. They're refreshing and give you healing antioxidants.

### Your 3-Day Detox Diet
Now that you know the principles, you're ready to take control when life throws you a dietary curve. The plan provides about 1,250 calories a day. Most refined sugars are eliminated to cut the craving for sweets. To placate your stretch receptors, there are plenty of plant-based foods that are rich in fiber. And delicious low- or no-cal drinks replace high-calorie cocktails. If you're not back to your normal healthy weight in 3 days, repeat for a total of 6 days.

| | BREAKFAST | SNACK | LUNCH | SNACK | DINNER | NUTRITION |
|---|---|---|---|---|---|---|
| **Day 1** | **Egg white–veggie scramble:** ½ cup egg whites (or 4 egg whites) with 1 cup chopped mixed vegetables (tomato, bell pepper, baby spinach), prepared with cooking spray<br>**1 slice toasted whole grain bread** or ½ whole wheat English muffin with 2 teaspoons 100% fruit spread<br>**1 cup 0% Greek yogurt**<br>**Coffee or tea** with ¼ cup fat-free milk | **1 sheet graham cracker** with 2 teaspoons natural (no added sugar) peanut butter | **Hummus-veggie pita sandwich:** ½ whole grain pita spread with 1 teaspoon deli mustard and 1 tablespoon hummus, then stuffed with vegetables (bell peppers, sprouts, lettuce, tomato) and 2 slices avocado<br>**1 medium orange** or 2 tangerines<br>**Unsweetened herbal tea** (hot or iced) with cinnamon stick | **1 piece fresh fruit** or 1 cup mixed vegetables with 2 teaspoons oil-and-vinegar dressing | **3 ounces grilled salmon** brushed with citrus glaze (1 tablespoon each orange juice, honey, and reduced-sodium soy sauce) while cooking<br>**½ cup cooked brown rice** prepared with 1 teaspoon olive oil<br>**1 cup cooked winter squash,** broccoli, or asparagus<br>**½ cup 0% plain Greek yogurt** with 2 teaspoons 100% fruit spread | 1,288 calories; 91 g protein; 181 g carb; 26 g total fat; 5 g saturated fat; 27 g fiber; 1,322 mg sodium |
| **Day 2** | **1 cup no-added-salt 1% cottage cheese** with ½ cup pineapple chunks<br>**5 whole grain crackers**<br>**Coffee or tea** with ¼ cup fat-free milk | **½ turkey sandwich:** 1 slice whole grain bread with 2 ounces low-sodium or reduced-sodium turkey breast, lettuce, tomato, and 1 teaspoon mustard | **Pasta tuna salad:** 1 cup cooked whole grain pasta spirals or bow ties with 1 cup chopped cherry tomatoes and tuna salad (4 ounces water-packed tuna mixed with 2 tablespoons chopped white onion, 1 tablespoon 0% Greek yogurt, and 2 teaspoons Dijon mustard)<br>**Water** with sprigs of mint or lemongrass | **1 medium orange** | **3 ounces broiled or grilled boneless chicken breast**<br>**1 baked sweet potato** topped with 2 teaspoons light spread<br>**2 cups tossed field greens** drizzled with 1 tablespoon vinaigrette dressing<br>**Unsweetened herbal tea** (hot or iced) with lemon | 1,242 calories; 122 g protein; 146 g carb; 22 g total fat; 4 g saturated fat; 26 g fiber; 1,565 mg sodium |
| **Day 3** | **1 cup cooked oatmeal** topped with ¼ cup 0% plain or vanilla Greek yogurt and 1 cup berries<br>**Coffee or tea** with ¼ cup fat-free milk | **1 ounce low-fat cheese** with 5 whole grain crackers | **1 cup low-sodium lentil or mine-strone soup**<br>**2 cups mixed salad greens** with ¼ cup low-sodium water-packed tuna or low-sodium diced turkey and 1 teaspoon olive oil with lemon juice or balsamic vinegar<br>**Unsweetened herbal tea** with cinnamon stick | **1 piece fresh fruit** (banana or apple) or 1 cup berries, with 8 ounces 0% plain or vanilla Greek yogurt | **Veggie burger** on whole wheat bun topped with 2 slices avocado<br>**Spinach salad:** 1½ cups baby spinach, ¼ cup sliced red onion, ¼ cup fresh mandarin orange slices, and 1 teaspoon olive oil with balsamic vinegar<br>**Seltzer water** with sliced lemon, orange, or lime | 1,277 calories; 86 g protein; 173 g carb; 32 g total fat; 5 g saturated fat; 34 g fiber; 1,577 mg sodium |

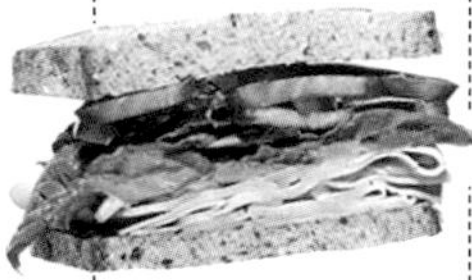

# ✳ PARTY FOOD POP QUIZ: PICK OR PASS?

There you are at your friend's party, virtuously dipping carrot sticks in hummus. But then the high-fat, sodium-packed hors d'oeuvres come out. Take this quiz to identify which item in each pair is the healthier choice.

## Chicken Wings or Pigs in a Blanket

## Olives or Candied Nuts

ANSWER

Choose the wings. The dogs have more saturated fat—40 percent of total fat versus 26 percent in the wings. And the "blanket" has white flour, which can contribute to insulin resistance.

ANSWER

Both contain healthy fats, but olives are the better pick. Six large olives set you back only 30 calories; 1 ounce of sweet nuts has about 170.

## Champagne Punch or Mulled Wine

**ANSWER**

Wine has little if any added sugar, so it has fewer calories than punch, which often combines fruit juices, sugar, and ginger ale with the bubbly.

## Mozzarella Sticks or Brie and Crackers

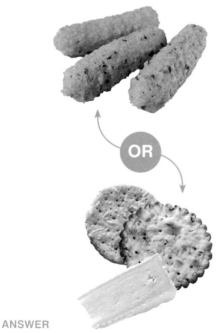

**ANSWER**

Bypass the gooey cheese sticks. A whole wheat cracker with ½ ounce of Brie has about half the calories and half the sodium of fried mozzarella, plus less fat.

## Spinach Dip or Mexican Seven-Layer Dip

**ANSWER**

Head for the border. The only beneficial ingredient in most spinach dips is the green stuff, but Mexican dip has nutritious beans, avocado, and salsa.

# ✳ HEALTHY-FOOD IMPOSTORS

This frozen entrée has as much salt as all these chips.

Movie popcorn can have as much fat (the bad, saturated kind) as five fast-food burgers.

A glass of cranberry juice cocktail can have more sugar than seven chocolate chip cookies.

## YOUR WORST DIET DAYS . . . SOLVED!

It's logical and routine to do certain tasks on certain days, such as grocery shopping on Saturday or laundry on Sunday. There are also certain days when it's harder to stick to a diet, according to scientists at Cornell University in Ithaca, New York. Here, some tips from the experts to help your diet survive the days when you're most tempted to give up.

### Monday
Chips and dip, burgers and fries, wine and cake—last weekend you went overboard, and now you're in withdrawal. Fill up on veggies and fruits so you can resist nutrient-poor snacks.

### Tuesday
Motivation flags. You started strong, but the grind is getting to you. Bribe yourself with scheduled smart snacks—protein can take the edge off hunger, so eat low-fat yogurt or a handful of almonds 1½ hours before a meal.

### Friday
Weekend fun begins, and you can't refuse dinner out with friends. Split a dish—many menu items are 1,000 calories or more.

## CAN PERFUME PEEL OFF POUNDS?

In a study done by Alan Hirsch, MD, neurological director of the Smell and Taste Treatment and Research Foundation in Chicago, people who smelled green apple, banana, or peppermint several times daily lost an average of 30 pounds in 6 months. "We think the scents may curb cravings," Dr. Hirsch says.

Try keeping a bottle of a favorite scent handy throughout the day and sniff instead of snacking.

Another strategy to avoid emotional eating is to calm down by sniffing orange or lavender fragrances. In an Austrian study, researchers wafted the smell of oranges before some participants and lavender before others. The two groups felt less anxious, more positive, and calmer when compared with participants who were exposed to no fragrance at all.

[ it worked for me ]

# 25 pounds lost!

## ❋ REILIN HARPER

In 2006, at her heaviest weight, Reilin was four sizes too big for her old stylish wardrobe. She dropped 25 pounds and got her pre-triplets body back.

### My Story

After delivering triplets in 2003, I was optimistic that before my boys' 1st birthday, I would shed the 30 pounds I'd gained. But all those feedings, diaper changes, and sleepless nights zapped my energy. Home-cooked meals became things of the past. Most nights after putting the boys down, my husband, Craig, and I would eat fast food on the couch.

As my boys grew, so did I. By the time they were 3, I'd packed 25 pounds onto my petite frame and gone up four sizes. One day while shopping at Kohl's, I couldn't zip up a single pair of size 14 jeans. I was devastated! I'd always been a trendy dresser who loved to shop, and now I was looking at a future of plus-size stretch pants. But instead of heading for the size 16s, I went to the gym the next day.

I started using the no-impact elliptical machine, slowly building my strength and endurance. The more time I

## VITAL STATS

Pounds lost: 25

Age: 43

Height: 5'3"

Weight then: 150 pounds

Weight now: 125 pounds

spent at the gym, the less self-conscious I felt, and I appreciated the newfound "me" time. My boys liked the gym's childcare center so much that some days it was their pleading that got me there.

Six months later and 10 pounds lighter, I ventured into a boot camp class. I loved it! I started taking the class twice a week, and the rest of the weight melted off. After 6 months of boot camp, I was down another 10 pounds.

Then I committed to training for a 5-K race. After a few weeks, I was hooked. I lost those final stubborn pounds, and I kept signing up for more races, which really kept me motivated. I even had the energy to cook several nights a week.

It's been 4 years since I lost 25 pounds and got back to my prebaby weight. My husband tells me that I look better now than I did when we got married. I'm toned and happy to flaunt it in skinny tops, short skirts, and leggings! I still love shopping, but these days, running is my favorite hobby.

## My Top Tips

* Start slowly but start . . . I started using the no-impact elliptical machine, slowly building my strength and endurance.

* Develop a support system . . . My boys liked the gym's childcare center so much that some days it was their pleading that got me there. Then my sister asked me to run a 5-K (3.1-mile) race with her.

* Cook more meals at home . . . After the triplets were born, I barely had the energy to eat fast food. Now that I have so much more energy, I cook meals several nights a week.

# Diet Disasters—Averted!

**Sometimes a carrot stick** is just a carrot stick. But too often, it's a crunchy orange vehicle for decadent dip—blue cheese, perhaps, or a nice herb ranch. As we dunk the sixth or seventh spear into that dressing, we might tell ourselves, "Well, at least I'm eating a hearty serving of veggies." True—but we're also consuming quite a lot of salt, fat, and calories. Wrecking otherwise healthy food picks may be part of our biology. In his book *The End of Overeating*, former FDA commissioner David Kessler, MD, explains that when you smell, see, or even think about "highly palatable" foods—ones that are high in fat, sugar, or salt—your brain can trigger the release of dopamine, the reward-seeking neurotransmitter. Just walking by a Krispy Kreme can cause your brain to send the "eat me" signal loud and clear. Biology doesn't have to be destiny, however. The fact is, it's possible to stop your pleasure-seeking brain from making menu decisions—you just need to know what to look for and be knowledgeable about what counts as a "pitfall."

## PLAN FOR SUCCESS

Eating smart involves more than selecting good-for-you foods; how you cook them and what goes on them can support—or sabotage—your best choices. Check out these common acts of food sabotage, plus easy strategies for steering clear of them, so that more often than not, you can keep delicious, healthy food top of mind, even in the face of temptation.

### The Sabotage
**You plunge your celery into peanut butter or creamy dip.**

While it may seem like a good idea to watch *Parenthood* with a plate of crisp crudités on the coffee table in front of you, that jar of peanut butter sitting right next to it can spell trouble. Sure, peanut butter provides healthy fat and protein, but it also has 94 calories per tablespoon—so this seemingly good-for-you snack can tip the scale in the wrong direction. And 2 tablespoons of creamy dressing can pack 145 calories and 15 grams of fat. "Eating just 100 calories more each day can translate to about a 10-pound weight gain over the course of a year," says Brian Wansink, PhD, director of Cornell University's Food and Brand Lab in Ithaca, New York, and author of *Mindless Eating*.

### The Healthy Move
If you're dying to dip, try the Crudités with Spicy Peanut Dipping Sauce on page 166, which has only 85 calories per serving. Or mix 0% plain Greek yogurt (it has about twice the protein of regular yogurt) with salsa or zingy seasonings such as horseradish or curry powder. Prepared hummus or black-bean dips coat raw veggies with protein, fiber, and flavor; just check the labels, because fat and calories can vary among brands. Finally, beat boredom by introducing new vegetables into your rotation, such as crunchy jicama or radishes that offer a naturally peppery bite.

### The Sabotage
**You choose "healthier" sweet potato fries as a side dish.**

Besides the beta-carotene (a disease-fighting carotenoid that our bodies convert to vitamin A) that's responsible for their vibrant color, sweet potatoes provide vitamin C, folate, potassium, and fiber—all for about 100 calories in a medium potato. But when you fry these and other vegetables (hello, broccoli bites and zucchini sticks), the fat and calorie counts skyrocket. Not only that, but a study in the *Journal of Food Science* found that certain vegetables, such as zucchini, actually lose some of their antioxidant power when fried.

### The Healthy Move
A baked sweet potato is the worry-free choice (mash in 2 tablespoons of a creamy fat-free dressing for extra flavor); eat the skin and you'll also get at least 4 grams of fiber. If you're just not satisfied with a baked spud, try Cajun Sweet Potato Fries on page 240 or buy a bag of oven-ready frozen fries at the supermarket. Compare labels and choose a brand that has no trans fat and no more than 0.5 gram of saturated fat per serving.

### The Sabotage
**You sauté your heart-smart fish in glugs of olive oil.**

Extra virgin olive oil is high in "good" monounsaturated fat—the kind of fat that can help lower LDL cholesterol—but it also has about 477 calories and 54 grams of fat per ¼ cup. If you don't measure the amount of oil you use to sauté, grill, broil, or roast, you can end up with way more than you need.

### The Healthy Move
Cook fish in the oven with a low-fat glaze. Not only is it supereasy, you use virtually no added oil. Try heart-healthy Roasted Salmon with Mustard-Dill Glaze on page 221.

When grilling or broiling, use a pastry brush or nonaerosol pump to lightly glaze food with oil, says Jennifer Nelson, RD, director of clinical dietetics and nutrition at the Mayo Clinic in Rochester, Minnesota. If you're making a stir-fry, wipe a paper towel dipped in olive oil around the wok before adding ingredients—or better yet, use a nonstick skillet.

You can also make your sautés sizzle with wine, soy sauce, chicken broth, or 100 percent carrot, tomato, or vegetable juice. And try poaching your fish in low-fat broth or watered-down orange juice; the fillets will soak

# ✳ WHAT'S WRONG WITH THIS PICTURE?

Having a side salad with your cheeseburger could lull you into thinking your meal is lower in calories than it is. In a recent study, participants were asked to estimate the number of calories in foods they believed were unhealthy. When fattening items (like a bacon-and-cheese sandwich on two waffles) were paired with a healthy item (like an apple), people guessed that the combo had fewer calories than the indulgent food alone. Dieters were three times more likely to fall into this trap, says study author Alexander Chernev, PhD, of Northwestern University in Evanston, Illinois. To keep your daily calorie counts accurate, use our online tracker at www.prevention.com/healthtracker.

up some of the liquid, which will make you feel fuller, says Barbara Rolls, PhD, professor of nutritional sciences at Pennsylvania State University in University Park and the author of *The Volumetrics Eating Plan*.

### The Sabotage
**You top your veggie-laden salad with cheese and nuts.**

The virtue of a salad starts to wilt when you add more than one calorie-dense topping, such as cheese, nuts, dried fruit, and croutons. Cheeses can register high in bad saturated fat, and though nuts have monounsaturated and polyunsaturated fats that may help raise "good" (HDL) cholesterol, a small serving of walnuts (about seven pieces) can add up to about 185 calories and 18 grams of fat. Plus, some add-ons are high in sodium.

### The Healthy Move
Nelson offers an easy-to-remember ratio for preparing entrée salads: "Three-quarters should be fresh fruits and vegetables, and the last quarter should be a combo of lean protein, like chicken, plus a complex carbohydrate, such as wheat berries or quinoa. Then allow yourself 2 tablespoons of calorie-dense items." For major nutrition impact with minimal calorie load, forgo dried fruit in favor of fresh pomegranate seeds; they're potent in polyphenols, and researchers at Case Western Reserve University in Cleveland found that pomegranate extract may be effective in reducing the inflammation that can lead to arthritis.

### The Sabotage
**You stir flavored syrup, whole milk, or whipped cream into coffee and tea.**

Sipping coffee or tea plain isn't a problem. In fact, both beverages have been linked to a number of health benefits, including a lower risk of heart disease and cancer. A study in the *Journal of Agricultural and Food Chemistry* also suggests that drinking coffee may reduce your risk of type 2 diabetes. But major calories and saturated fat come with added ingredients such as sugary syrups, honey, whipped cream, and whole milk

(1% and 2% aren't much better). For about the same 450 calories in a large Iced Mocha Raspberry Latte at Dunkin' Donuts, for instance, you can eat two slices of Pizza Hut's hand-tossed pepperoni pizza. And while honey may seem like a natural, healthier alternative to sugar, the fact is it has 21 calories per teaspoon versus sugar's 16.

## The Healthy Move

For a low-cal, lower-fat drink that feels like a sweet treat, choose coffee beans in tempting flavors such as chocolate almond, hazelnut, or white chocolate, rather than using syrupy mix-ins after brewing, and lighten your coffee with fat-free milk. Teas, too, come in sweet vanilla, berry, and tropical fruit blends. And whether you use Splenda, sugar, or honey in your beverages, limit yourself to about a teaspoon.

## The Sabotage

**You smother your grilled chicken sandwich or turkey burger in barbecue sauce.**

You're wise to choose skinless grilled chicken, but be careful with condiments. Bottled barbecue sauce is filled with sugar, which means calories (about 94 per ¼ cup).

## The Healthy Move

Ditch the high-sugar sauce and instead spice up chicken by marinating it in cayenne pepper sauce, or mix hot sauce with some fat-free yogurt and smear it on your sandwich for Buffalo-inspired flavor. When you're really craving the "Q," make the Barbecued Chicken Sandwiches on page 109, which pack big flavor with far less sugar than bottled sauce.

Another way to punch up the taste and nutrient power of grilled chicken sandwiches and turkey burgers: Top them with homemade slaw. Bagged shredded cabbage makes a convenient base; toss it with flavored vinegar or fat-free mayo and a little mustard. At 11 calories per ½ cup, raw cabbage offers filling fiber and vitamins such as C and $B_6$, and as a cruciferous veggie, it contains cancer-fighting antioxidants.

## THE ORGANIC CALORIE CONUNDRUM

When you want a treat, don't judge a cookie by its label. According to a recent study, people believe that organic cookies contain 40 percent fewer calories than regular—a myth that can lead to overeating. The term *organic* creates a health halo, says Jenny Lee of the Cornell University Food and Brand Lab in Ithaca, New York. And while the glow may be deserved for fruits and vegetables (several studies show that organic versions contain more nutrients than conventionally grown), not so for packaged foods. "Organic" cookies may contain ingredients grown without conventional pesticides, but in some cases they have more calories. Treat organic cookies like any other dessert—enjoy them in moderation.

**325**

Calories
*in 5 cookies*

**Newman's Own Organic Newman-Os**

**267**

Calories
*in 5 cookies*

**Oreo Sandwich Cookies**

# ✱ FINE PRINT: LABEL FACTS AND FICTION

Flavored yogurt is popular and convenient—but does it deserve its health halo?

**7**
**PACKETS OF SUGAR:**
the amount of sweetener in this 4-ounce container

**Half-Hearted**
Potassium lowers blood pressure, but a small banana has more than twice this amount.

**Go Greek**
If you switch to plain Greek yogurt, you'll get more than double the protein.

**Faux Fruit**
This yogurt has pureed fruit—rather than the real thing—and nearly no vitamin C.

**Bone Boost**
This is a hearty dose of cancer-fighting vitamin D and bone-boosting calcium.

**Culture Vulture**
Don't be swayed by "special" additions. Probiotics (i.e., live cultures) are good for digestion, but all yogurts contain plenty.

### Nutrition Facts
Serving Size 1 container (113g)
Servings Per Package 4

**Amount Per Serving**

Calories 110   Calories from Fat 15

% Daily Value*

| | |
|---|---|
| **Total Fat** 2g | 3% |
| Saturated Fat 1g | 5% |
| Trans Fat 0g | |
| **Cholesterol** 10 mg | 2% |
| **Sodium** 65mg | 3% |
| **Potassium** 220mg | 4% |
| **Total Carbohydrate** 19g | 8% |
| Sugars 19g | |
| **Protein** 5g | 6% |
| Calcium 15%   Vitamin D 15% | |

Not a significant source of Dietary Fiber, Vitamin A, Vitamin C and Iron.

*Percent Daily Values are based on a 2,000 calorie diet.

INGREDIENTS: CULTURED GRADE A REDUCED-FAT MILK, FRUCTOSE, SUGAR, STRAWBERRY AND BLUEBERRY PUREE, WATER, CONTAINS LESS THAN 1% OF WHEY PROTEIN CONCENTRATE, CORN STARCH, MODIFIED CORN STARCH, KOSHER GELATIN, NATURAL FLAVOR, CARMINE (FOR COLOR), MALIC ACID, SODIUM CITRATE. CONTAINS LIVE AND ACTIVE CULTURES.

**Say yes to yogurt,** as long as it's plain. Nearly 75 percent of yogurt eaters opt for fruity flavors, but to get your fill of protein, probiotics, vitamin D, and calcium—without the additives and sugar—choose unflavored yogurt and mix in fresh fruit.

## WHEN WALKING MAKES YOU FAT

**Pop quiz:** Would you lose more weight if you curled up with a good book or if you took a leisurely walk? The end result is about the same *unless* your walk is fast enough to leave you breathless. In a new study from Harvard University, women who strolled at a window-shopping pace throughout a 16-year period weighed about the same as women who didn't exercise at all. But the women who stepped up the pace to 4 mph (around 130 steps a minute) fared better at fighting age-related weight gain.

## DITCH THE DIET PILLS

"Dietary supplements may represent the next big drug safety catastrophe," says Steven Nissen, MD, a cardiologist at the Cleveland Clinic and a *Prevention* advisory board member. "We don't know exactly what most supplements contain, so we don't know if they're actually safe." More and more, weight-loss products are being "adulterated" with potentially dangerous ingredients. "Originally, the makers would throw in something like caffeine to give you a kick," says Tod Cooperman, MD, president of ConsumerLab.com. "Now they're adding in

compounds you find in prescription drugs without including that information on their labels." Some of these products—which are most often sold on the Internet so the manufacturers can evade regulators—may include versions of Meridia, Viagra, Cialis, or Levitra without consumers' knowledge.

The other thing consumers don't realize is that adulterated products can be far riskier than prescription diet pills. If you'd had a prescription for Meridia you would have been under a doctor's care and aware of how much sibutramine you were taking, as well as what side effects you might expect, because they were listed on the label.

In recent years, the FDA has gone after more than 70 tainted weight-loss products, many with names like Slim Burn, 24 Hours Diet, and Natural Model, after finding that they had been adulterated with undeclared stimulants, diuretics, and antidepressants, often in amounts exceeding the maximum recommended dosages at which such drugs can be prescribed.

Sometimes the additives aren't legal even with a prescription. For example, one supplement targeted by the FDA contained fenproporex, a stimulant not approved in the United States because it can cause arrhythmia and possibly even sudden death.

In addition, these products often are not effective for the conditions for which they're advertised and may divert patients from legitimate medications, according to Dr. Nissen. If they do seem to be making a difference, that may be cause for concern, too. "If a weight-loss supplement is working, it could be due to a stimulant whose safety is unproven," says Arthur Agatston, MD, a cardiologist and member of the *Prevention* advisory board. "Even if you lose weight, you may have unpleasant, even dangerous cardiac side effects. There's no diet supplement or drug that I know of that's safe and effective long term." What's more, according to Dr. Nissen, even if you do lose weight by using a drug or supplement, research suggests that once you stop taking the product, you will gain back the weight and may be at greater risk of a heart attack or stroke. Both physicians recommend a healthy diet and regular exercise as the only sustainable way to lose weight and stay healthy.

[ it worked for me ]

# 20 pounds lost!

## ✳ LAURA WOOSTER BALDWIN

Experimenting with veganism brought permanent weight loss and improved health.

### My Story

The year after I got married, my weight jumped from 120 to 135, and those 15 pounds made a big difference on my 5-foot-3 frame. Although I wasn't pigging out on junk food, I didn't exactly have the healthiest diet—I rarely, if ever, ate vegetables. So I made a 2009 New Year's resolution: I'd try the popular Blue Print Cleanse for 4 days (drinking only fruit and vegetable juices), then cut all animal products out of my diet for the next 3 months.

My British husband was not about to give up meat, but he was very supportive of my decision—so I cooked and he ate. I made stews stuffed with chickpeas, tomatoes, and seitan (wheat gluten). I roasted onions, garlic, broccoli, peppers, and other veggies to bring out their sweetness. I found delicious soy-free vegan sausages, which I made with kale and polenta. I was loving the food—and the results. Three months passed, and I never looked back.

Pounds lost: 20

Age: 35

Height: 5'3"

Weight then: 135 pounds

Weight now: 115 pounds

I was back at my old weight of 120 pounds before my 3-month vegan trial ended—and I've held steady at 115 pounds for 2½ years. Before, I was a horrendous cook, but vegetables are a lot more forgiving than meats, so now I'm more confident in the kitchen. The best part is how I feel: Now that my meals consist of nutritious foods, I feel and look healthier all around.

## My Top Tips

✳ Nourish your curiosity . . . Because I was willing to try veganism, I was able to improve not only my weight and my health but also my cooking skills.

✳ Be sure to take your daily vitamins—especially B$_{12}$.

✳ Before dining out, go online to review the restaurant menu. A lot of times there are dishes that can be modified for vegans, but it helps to know what you're getting into and if you should eat a big lunch.

✳ Always carry around a snack like some nuts or vegan nutrition bars. You never know.

# Pure & Powerful: Foods to Rev Up Your Metabolism

**Food used to be simple.** You ate what you grew on the land or bought from nearby farmers. Today food is much more complicated, and we're both better and worse off for it. We can eat a greater variety of healthy foods than our ancestors did—think fresh berries in winter—but we can also eat a lot more highly processed ones. And that fare seems to be winning the day, if our epidemics of obesity and diabetes are any indication.

But an increasing trend toward clean eating—which emphasizes whole, fresh, traditional fare—could mark a turning point in our sometimes dysfunctional relationship with food and help us achieve good health, ideal weight, and culinary satisfaction.

To assist you in buying the best foods and reaping the potential weight-loss and disease-fighting benefits, we created Nine Easy Ways to Clean Up Your Diet, as well as a handy shopping chart of the 50 healthiest everyday foods. In no time, you'll be eating clean—and lean.

# NINE EASY WAYS TO CLEAN UP YOUR DIET

These simple rules will have you eating less junk and fewer hidden calories, so you can slim down and stay healthy naturally.

## 1. Toss a Few Heavily Processed Staples

Instead of overhauling your pantry all at once, start by eliminating corn oil products and soda—both are highly processed, says Nina Planck, the author of *Real Food: What to Eat and Why.* "That alone," she says, "is a huge first step." Another easy step is replacing white flour breads and pastas with ones made from whole grains.

## 2. Clean Up the Biggest Part of Your Diet

To keep it simple, assess what part of your diet supplies the most calories, says Mary Ellen Camire, PhD, professor of food science and human nutrition at the University of Maine in Orono. If you're an omnivore, buy meat that comes from grass-fed cattle and eggs from pasture-raised chickens, but stick to conventional produce instead of organic. If you're a vegetarian, buying organic produce makes more sense.

## 3. Shop the Perimeter of the Supermarket

Most whole, natural foods are on the outside aisles of grocery stores—that's where the produce, dairy, and meat sections usually are. As you go deeper into the center of the store, you encounter more processed and packaged food. "Find the stuff that spoils," says nutritionist Johnny Bowden, PhD, the author of *The Most Effective Ways to Live Longer.*

## 4. Read Labels

It's the easiest way to distinguish a "clean" food from a highly processed one. Think about it: A totally natural head of lettuce has no label, while a bag of highly processed ranch-flavored corn chips has a dozen or more ingredients. Instead of eliminating all processed foods, study the labels on the packaging, and choose foods with fewer and simpler ingredients. Avoid hydrogenated oils, artificial flavors and colors, stabilizers, preservatives, excessive amounts of fat and sodium, and added refined sugar.

## 5. Think Nutrients per Serving

Consider the amount of nutrients in a product rather than focusing solely on price. Ask yourself if the cost of the food is worth the nutrients or lack thereof. You can make this assessment on every item by comparing the amounts of protein, fiber, minerals, and vitamins against fat, sodium, sugars, and chemical additives. Some clean eaters also focus on environmental impact. Some stores are promising to make the assessment easier—Walmart is phasing in a sustainable product index designed to help consumers judge at a glance the environmental impact of a product, including food.

An organization called the Ecological Food Manufacturers Association (EFMA) is pushing companies to go even further. "A consumer should be able to pick up a product and, by looking at one little score, instantly know how safe, planet-friendly, and nutritious it is," says EFMA founder and CEO Winston Riley. NuVal, a food rating system designed by David Katz, MD, MPH, and other medical experts, which gives points to foods based on their nutritional content, is available in more than 500 supermarkets nationwide. The higher the score, the cleaner the food. You may want to visit GoodGuide (www.goodguide.com) to view health, environment, and social responsibility information, plus ratings, on more than 90,000 products. GoodGuide is also available as a free app for the iPhone.

## 6. Cook More Meals at Home

This is an easy way to shift more of your resources toward whole food and potentially save money. Plus, many restaurants rely on highly processed food to create their meals. To make home cooking easier, master a few one-pot or one-pan dishes with simple ingredients that you can whip up quickly and will feed the family for days. "In my fridge right now, I have some beef chili and meat loaf," says Planck, a mother of three. "Each makes a wholesome meal with plenty of leftovers." Cooking helps you appreciate and enjoy your food more, especially if you share the process with others, says Michael Pollan, the author of *The*

*Omnivore's Dilemma* and *In Defense of Food*. He recommends involving family members by giving them jobs, such as chopping foods and setting the table. As a bonus, he notes that people who cook tend to eat more healthfully and weigh less than those who don't.

## 7. Adjust Your Tastebuds

If you're accustomed to eating food with lots of salt, sugar, fat, and other additives, you'll need to retrain your tastebuds to appreciate the more subtle flavors of whole foods. For instance, if you don't like the taste of brown rice, mix it with white rice in decreasing amounts until you adapt. You can do the same thing with whole grain pasta and white pasta. It works for salty and fatty foods,

too. Instead of switching immediately to, say, low-sodium soups, mix a regular can with a low-sodium version, and adjust the ratio toward less sodium as you get used to the flavor. It can take up to 12 weeks to adjust, says Richard Mattes, MPH, PhD, professor of foods and nutrition at Purdue University in West Lafayette, Indiana.

## 8. Follow an 80-20 Strategy

Eating plans go bad—and are eventually abandoned—when they turn obsessive. Clean eating is no different. To avoid that trap, take an 80-20 approach; that is, try to eat natural food 80 percent of the time, with a 20 percent buffer for when you're traveling, socializing, or simply can't.

### 9. Feel the Love

For Dr. Camire, clean eating is all about the pleasures of food. She remembers some advice that cookbook author and Food Network host Alton Brown delivered at an Institute of Food Technologists conference a few years ago. "I'll never forget it," she says. "He said, 'You know, as long as it's made with love . . .' That really stuck with me because it goes back to the whole French paradox thing: While the French are talking with family, drinking wine, and turning eating into a celebration, we're scarfing down handheld food in our cars. His message was to think about where your food is coming from, who's preparing it, and—especially—how you're eating it."

In other words, be mindful. It's a word that comes up repeatedly in discussions of clean eating. Be more mindful of how you shop for foods, how you cook meals, and how you eat.

"I choose to eat this way for many reasons, and one of the biggest is enjoyment," says Pollan. "There doesn't have to be a trade-off between pleasure and health. If you eat this way, you can have both. It's not rocket science. In fact, it's not even science—it's just common sense."

# ✳ THE 50 HEALTHIEST EVERYDAY FOODS

The journey from fresh to processed is not a simple one—and eating completely clean at every meal isn't always realistic. That's why we compiled this chart to show how common foods morph from real to highly processed. Your goal: Choose from foods in their natural state as often as possible, go with foods that are somewhat processed in a pinch, and limit highly processed items.

| NATURAL STATE 1ST CHOICE | SOMEWHAT PROCESSED 2ND CHOICE | HIGHLY PROCESSED LIMIT | SHOPPING TIP |
|---|---|---|---|
| APPLE | APPLESAUCE | APPLE TOASTER PASTRY | Applesauce is a healthy choice, but it has fewer nutrients than a whole apple. |
| ORANGE | 100% ORANGE JUICE | ORANGE DRINK | Many fruit drinks contain high fructose corn syrup and little real juice. |
| FRESH STRAWBERRIES | STRAWBERRY PRESERVES | STRAWBERRY GELATIN DESSERT | Gelatin desserts usually contain artificial strawberry flavor, not real fruit. |
| PEACH | CANNED PEACHES IN 100% JUICE | CANNED PEACHES IN HEAVY SYRUP | Fruit canned in heavy syrup has more sugar and calories than fresh. |
| FRESH FIGS | FIG PRESERVES | FIG SANDWICH COOKIES | Packaged fruit cookies may contain refined sugar and preservatives. |
| PINEAPPLE | CANNED DICED PINEAPPLE | PINEAPPLE COCKTAIL CUP | Fresh pineapple is higher in vitamins A and C and beta-carotene than canned. |
| CORN ON THE COB | CORN TORTILLA CHIPS | CORN FLAKES | Buy tortilla chips with just three ingredients: whole corn, oil, and salt—and eat them in moderation. |

| NATURAL STATE 1ST CHOICE | SOMEWHAT PROCESSED 2ND CHOICE | HIGHLY PROCESSED LIMIT | SHOPPING TIP |
|---|---|---|---|
| SPINACH | BAGGED PREWASHED SPINACH | FROZEN CREAMED SPINACH | Avoid frozen veggies in sodium-rich sauces. Buy plain and add your own light sauce. |
| GARLIC | JARRED MINCED GARLIC | BOTTLED GARLIC MARINADE | Minced fresh garlic is cheaper and more flavorful than jarred. |
| CARROTS | BABY CARROTS | FROZEN HONEY-GLAZED CARROTS | Baby carrots are healthy but cost more than regular carrots. |
| SOUP FROM SCRATCH | CANNED SOUP | DEHYDRATED SOUP MIX | Homemade soup often has less sodium and more flavor than canned. |
| HERITAGE HAM | DELI HAM | PACKAGED DELI BOLOGNA | Heritage varieties of pork are much less likely to contain hormones than factory meat is. |
| WHOLE TURKEY | DELI TURKEY | TURKEY MEATBALLS | If you buy deli meat, ask for brands free of fillers and nitrates. |
| GRASS-FED BEEF | GRAIN-FED BEEF | FROZEN BEEF PATTIES | Grass-fed meat is higher in nutrients and lower in fat than grain-fed beef. |
| FRESH CHICKEN BREASTS | DELI-SLICED CHICKEN | CHICKEN NUGGETS | Chicken nuggets contain very little real chicken. |

Pure & Powerful: Foods to
Rev Up Your Metabolism

| NATURAL STATE 1ST CHOICE | SOMEWHAT PROCESSED 2ND CHOICE | HIGHLY PROCESSED LIMIT | SHOPPING TIP |
|---|---|---|---|
| PASTURE-RAISED EGGS → | OMEGA-3-FORTIFIED EGGS → | EGG BEATERS | Pasture-raised eggs may have 60% more vitamin A and 200% more omega-3s than regular eggs. |
| CREAM → | FAT-FREE HALF CREAM/ HALF MILK → | FLAVORED DAIRY CREAMER | Flavored dairy creamers are often made with colorings, artificial flavors, and corn syrup. |
| PLAIN YOGURT → | FLAVORED YOGURT → | FLAVORED YOGURT DRINK | Buy plain yogurt and flavor It at home with honey or fresh fruit. |
| WHOLE GRAIN BREAD → | WHEAT BREAD → | FORTIFIED WHITE BREAD | If a whole grain isn't the first ingredient, you're missing out on nutrients. |
| DRIED WHOLE WHEAT PASTA → | DRIED WHITE PASTA → | INSTANT NOODLES | Whole grain pasta is higher in antioxidants than white pasta or instant noodles. |
| BROWN RICE → | WHITE RICE → | FLAVORED INSTANT RICE | Brown rice, unlike white, hasn't had its fiber-rich layers of bran and germ removed. |
| PEANUTS → | NATURAL PEANUT BUTTER → | PROCESSED PEANUT BUTTER | Natural peanut butter should contain only peanuts and a dash of salt. |
| FRESH EDAMAME → | TOFU → | FROZEN VEGGIE BURGERS | Frozen veggie burgers are vegetarian-friendly but are highly processed. |

Pure & Powerful: Foods to Rev Up Your Metabolism

## FRUITS AND VEGGIES

Produce picked and frozen at peak ripeness has just as many nutrients and antioxidants as fresh, if not more.

* Dole Wildly Nutritious Signature Blends frozen mixed berries
* Cascadian Farm Organic frozen cut spinach

## CEREALS

Simplicity is key for these three brands: minimal processing and few additives.

* Bear Naked 100% Pure & Natural Cranberry Raisin Cereal
* Arrowhead Mills Organic Steel Cut Oats Hot Cereal
* Post Shredded Wheat cereal

## DAIRY

These brands are made from milk that's free of antibiotics and hormones.

* Stonyfield Farm Organic yogurt
* Organic Valley 1% milk

## MEALS

These items let their ingredients' natural flavors speak for themselves—no refined sugar or excessive fat or salt.

* Birds Eye Asparagus Stir-Fry
* Annie's Homegrown Organic Whole Wheat Shells & White Cheddar
* Kashi All-Natural Tuscan Veggie Bake

## PANTRY STAPLES

These products make it easy and delicious to incorporate whole grains and omega-3s into your diet.

* Uncle Ben's Fast & Natural Whole Grain Instant Brown Rice
* Ronzoni Healthy Harvest Whole Wheat Blend Spaghetti
* Colavita Extra Virgin Olive Oil

## PACKAGED FOODS WE LOVE

You don't have to sacrifice convenience or your budget to eat clean. More companies are producing foods that are relatively unprocessed and more healthful. We asked our experts to recommend their favorites—the foods they grab off supermarket shelves when they don't have time to cook from scratch.

# ✳ BOOST ANTIOXIDANTS AT ANY MEAL

Herbs and spices can deliver just as much disease-fighting punch as fruits and veggies, says Cheryl Forberg, RD, the author of *Positively Ageless*. Here, how to add low-calorie flavor while dramatically boosting your antioxidant intake. Scores per ½ teaspoon are in ORAC points, a measure of antioxidants in food. As a comparison, a ½-cup serving of blueberries has an ORAC score of 3,502.

**Tarragon, fresh**
Score: 155
Add to scrambled eggs.

**Cinnamon, ground**
Score: 1,752
Add to oatmeal, French toast, or applesauce.

**Thyme, fresh**
Score: 137
Add to fresh orange slices with black pepper and olive oil.

**Oregano, dried**
Score: 1,753
Add to tomato bruschetta or chicken breast marinated in olive oil and garlic.

**Sage, fresh**
Score: 320
Add to cornbread and stuffings.

**Cloves, ground**
Score: 2,903
Add to mashed sweet potatoes or acorn squash.

**Turmeric**
Score: 1,271
Add to curries or bulgur salad with chickpeas and currants.

* Pacific Natural Foods Organic Free Range Chicken Broth
* Bumble Bee skinless and boneless pink salmon

## BREADS

Sprouted grain bread contains more than twice the dietary fiber of white or wheat bread.

* Food for Life 7 Sprouted Grains Bread
* Alvarado St. Bakery Sprouted Multi-Grain Bread

## SNACKS, CONDIMENTS, AND SPREADS

From the one ingredient in Crazy Richard's peanut butter—peanuts—to the blend of raw fruits, nuts, and spices in the Lärabar, these snacks are as real as processed gets.

* Lärabar energy bars
* Snyder's of Hanover Sourdough Hard Pretzels
* St. Dalfour black cherry 100% fruit spread
* Crazy Richard's 100% Natural Chunky Peanut Butter
* Guiltless Gourmet Mild Black Bean Dip
* Wholly Guacamole Classic
* Sabra Classic Hummus
* San Marcos Chipotle Peppers in Adobo Sauce
* Drew's All Natural Organic Salsa

## DESSERTS

* Häagen-Dazs fat-free mango sorbet

# ✳ METABOLISM BOOSTER!

**Hot Peppers**

SPICE UP TO SLIM DOWN

Capsaicin, the compound that gives hot peppers their kick, raises your core body temperature, causing you to burn more calories, according to the *International Journal of Obesity*. Hotter peppers have a greater effect, so use the spiciest one you can stand in chili, curries, or sauces.

| | |
|---|---|
| Pure capsaicin | Burn off your tongue! |
| Habanero | Superhot |
| Cayenne | Hot |
| Serrano | |
| Chipotle | |
| Original Tabasco Brand Pepper Sauce | Medium |
| Jalapeño | |
| Poblano | |
| Pimiento | Mild |

# Recipes That Slim & Satisfy

**Let's get cooking!** The more than 200 family-pleasing recipes in this collection have been perfected by the Prevention Test Kitchen so you know they're foolproof. From morning until night, we have your meals covered with the likes of Double Tomato and Turkey Bacon Omelet, Crunchy French Toast with Raspberry Fruit Spread, Barbecued Chicken Sandwiches, Chipotle Crab and Avocado Salad, Fettuccine and Meatballs, San Antonio Turkey Fajitas, Pineapple-Glazed Pork Chops, Cappuccino Pudding Cake, and Apple Crumb Pie. The only problem you'll have is choosing what to eat first.

# breakfasts

# Mexican Egg-and-Spinach Bake

2 whole grain pitas (6" diameter), halved horizontally

5 teaspoons extra virgin olive oil, divided

1 bag (5 ounces) baby spinach

2 large plum tomatoes, thinly sliced

2 tablespoons fresh cilantro

4 eggs

¼ teaspoon salt

¼ teaspoon pepper

½ cup crumbled reduced-fat queso blanco

PREHEAT the oven to 450°F. Place the pitas, cut side up, on a baking sheet.

BRUSH with 4 teaspoons of the oil. Bake for about 5 minutes, or until starting to brown.

MEANWHILE, heat the remaining 1 teaspoon oil in a large nonstick skillet over medium heat. Cook and stir the spinach for about 3 minutes, or until wilted.

DIVIDE the spinach, tomatoes, and cilantro evenly among the pitas, leaving an empty space in the centers. Place an egg in the center of each pita. Sprinkle with the salt and pepper. Bake for about 8 minutes, or until the yolks are lightly set. Sprinkle with the cheese and bake for about 2 minutes, or until the cheese softens.

---

Total time: 25 minutes ✳ Makes 4 servings

Per serving: 254 calories,13 g protein, 25 g carbohydrates, 13 g total fat, 3 g saturated fat, 5 g fiber, 545 mg sodium

Building your breakfast on half of a pita cuts the calories, but with all the tasty toppings, you won't miss the extra bread.

# More-Vegetable-Than-Egg Frittata

2 tablespoons olive oil, divided

½ onion, sliced

4 cups mixed cut-up vegetables, such as sliced Swiss chard, cut-up asparagus, and chopped zucchini

1 teaspoon salt, divided

¼ cup fresh basil leaves, loosely torn

3 eggs

½ cup grated Parmesan cheese

¼ teaspoon pepper

PREHEAT the broiler.

HEAT 1 tablespoon of the oil in a medium nonstick skillet over medium heat. Cook and stir the onion for about 3 minutes, or until soft. Add the vegetables and ¼ teaspoon of the salt. Increase the heat to medium-high and cook, stirring occasionally, for about 12 minutes, or until the pan is almost dry. Decrease the heat as necessary so the vegetables brown without scorching. Stir in the basil.

MEANWHILE, in a medium bowl, whisk together the eggs, cheese, pepper, and the remaining ¾ teaspoon salt. Add the remaining 1 tablespoon oil to the pan. Pour the egg mixture evenly over the vegetables. Cook, without stirring, for about 10 minutes, or until the eggs are barely set.

BROIL for about 2 minutes, or until lightly browned.

---

Total time: 35 minutes  ✻  Makes 4 servings

Per serving: 188 calories, 11 g protein, 6 g carbohydrates, 14 g total fat, 4 g saturated fat, 2 g fiber, 860 mg sodium

A frittata is a great way to use leftover vegetables. Instead of 4 cups raw veggies, add about 2 cups cooked vegetables to the onions, give a couple of good stirs, and then proceed with the recipe.

# Sweet Potato and Pea Frittata

2 sweet potatoes, cut into ½" chunks

4 eggs

2 egg whites

¼ cup fat-free milk

¼ teaspoon salt

¼ teaspoon pepper

3 slices reduced-sodium center-cut bacon, chopped

1 sweet onion, chopped

¼ teaspoon dried thyme

1 cup frozen baby peas

PREHEAT the oven to 500°F. Place the potatoes in a saucepan over high heat with enough cold water to cover by 2". Bring to a boil and cook for 8 minutes, or until tender. Drain.

IN a medium bowl, beat together the eggs, egg whites, milk, salt, and pepper until smooth.

MEANWHILE, cook the bacon in an ovenproof medium nonstick skillet over medium-high heat for about 3 minutes, or until starting to crisp. If the skillet handle is not ovenproof, wrap in a double layer of foil. Stir in the onion and thyme and cook for about 2 minutes, or until starting to soften. Stir in the peas and cook for 2 minutes, or until thawed. Add the potatoes and cook for 1 minute. Pour in the egg mixture and cook, stirring occasionally, for 2 minutes. Reduce the heat to medium and cook, without stirring, for about 4 minutes, or until almost set.

BAKE for about 5 minutes, or until set and browned.

--------------------------------------------------

Total time: 35 minutes  ✱  Makes 4 servings

Per serving: 248 calories, 15 g protein, 30 g carbohydrates, 8 g total fat, 2 g saturated fat, 5 g fiber, 389 mg sodium

## NUTRITION NEWS TO USE

Power up omelets and frittatas by eating eggs fresh off the farm. Researchers at Pennsylvania State University found that pasture-raised hens produce eggs with higher levels of essential nutrients than caged hens do. Pastured eggs have double the vitamin E, which strengthens your immune system, and 2½ times as much omega-3 fatty acids, the nutritional heroes that aid your vision, brain functioning, and heart.

# Quiche Florentine

3 tablespoons plain dry bread crumbs

4 ounces fresh mushrooms, sliced

¼ small onion, chopped

¼ teaspoon dried thyme

5 ounces frozen spinach, thawed and squeezed dry

1 tablespoon all-purpose flour

⅓ cup 1% cottage cheese

¼ cup shredded reduced-fat Swiss cheese

1 can (12 ounces) evaporated fat-free milk

3 eggs

¼ teaspoon salt

¼ teaspoon pepper

**PREHEAT** the oven to 350°F. Coat a 9" nonstick pie pan with cooking spray. Sprinkle the bread crumbs evenly over the bottom and side of the pan.

**COAT** a large nonstick skillet with cooking spray. Heat over medium heat. Cook the mushrooms, onion, and thyme, covered, for 3 minutes, or until the mushrooms are soft.

**STIR** in the spinach and cook, uncovered, for about 3 minutes, or until dry. Stir in the flour and cook for 1 minute. Remove from the heat and stir in the cottage cheese and Swiss.

**IN** a medium bowl, beat together the milk, eggs, salt, and pepper. Stir in the spinach mixture. Pour into the pie pan.

**BAKE** for about 35 minutes, or until lightly browned and a knife inserted in the center comes out clean. Cool in the pan on a rack for 5 minutes.

---

Total time: 55 minutes   ✱   Makes 4 servings

Per serving: 199 calories, 18 g protein, 19 g carbohydrates, 6 g total fat, 3 g saturated fat, 1 g fiber, 448 mg sodium

Leftover quiche wedges—cold or gently reheated in the microwave oven—make a wonderful weekday breakfast. Cool, cover, and refrigerate the baked quiche for several days.

# Artichoke, Mushroom, and Goat Cheese Omelet

1 package (9 ounces) frozen artichoke hearts

2 tablespoons olive oil

1 onion, halved and thinly sliced

6 ounces fresh mushrooms, sliced

3 eggs

3 egg whites

2 tablespoons fat-free milk

2 tablespoons chopped fresh parsley

2 tablespoons finely chopped fresh chives (optional)

¼ teaspoon salt

¼ teaspoon pepper

½ cup crumbled goat cheese

PREHEAT the broiler.

COOK the artichokes according to package directions. Drain. Pat dry and set aside.

HEAT the oil in a medium ovenproof nonstick skillet over medium heat. Cook the onion, stirring occasionally, for about 4 minutes, or until tender. Add the artichokes and mushrooms. Cook, stirring often, for about 6 minutes, or until the vegetables are tender and lightly browned.

MEANWHILE, in a medium bowl, whisk together the eggs, egg whites, milk, parsley, chives (if using), salt, and pepper. Pour into the pan. Reduce the heat to low and cook, lifting the edges to allow the uncooked egg to run underneath, for about 3 minutes, or until the bottom is set but the top is still runny.

DOT with the cheese. If the skillet handle isn't ovenproof, wrap in a double layer of foil.

BROIL for about 3 minutes, or until the eggs are set.

Total time: 25 minutes ✻ Makes 4 servings

Per serving: 231 calories, 14 g protein, 11 g carbohydrates, 16 g total fat, 5 g saturated fat, 5 g fiber, 361 mg sodium

A sophisticated breakfast dish, this open-faced omelet would also be welcome for brunch or a light supper.

# Creamy Scrambled Eggs with Smoked Trout

1 teaspoon olive oil

3 eggs, lightly beaten

1 ounce smoked trout, cut into thin strips

1 tablespoon finely chopped fresh chives

Pinch of ground red pepper (optional)

2 tablespoons fat-free sour cream

**HEAT** the oil in a nonstick skillet over medium-high heat for about 1 minute. Cook the eggs for 10 seconds, or until set on the bottom. Sprinkle with the trout, chives, and pepper (if using). Cook and stir gently for about 1 minute, or until scrambled. Remove from the heat and gently stir in the sour cream.

---

Total time: 10 minutes ✳ Makes 2 servings

Per serving: 165 calories, 13 g protein, 4 g carbohydrates, 11 g total fat, 3 g saturated fat, 0 g fiber, 198 mg sodium

This easy dish makes a special weekend breakfast or brunch. Look for the trout in a delicatessen or supermarket with a good smoked fish selection, but feel free to replace it with smoked salmon.

# Double Tomato and Turkey Bacon Omelet

6 sun-dried tomato halves

1 thin strip turkey bacon

2 plum tomatoes, quartered lengthwise and thinly sliced

1½ tablespoons crumbled reduced-fat goat cheese

2 eggs

3 egg whites

1 tablespoon water

1 scallion, all parts, thinly sliced

¼ teaspoon pepper

1 teaspoon olive oil, divided

IN a small bowl, combine the sun-dried tomatoes with enough boiling water to cover. Let stand for 15 minutes, or until softened.

COOK the bacon according to package directions. Crumble and set aside.

DRAIN the sun-dried tomatoes and chop. Return to the bowl and stir in the plum tomatoes, cheese, and reserved bacon.

IN a medium bowl, whisk together the eggs, egg whites, water, scallion, and pepper until slightly frothy.

HEAT ½ teaspoon of the oil in a medium nonstick skillet over medium heat. Cook half of the egg mixture, occasionally lifting the edges with a spatula and tilting the pan to allow the uncooked mixture to flow underneath, for 2 minutes, or until almost set. Spoon half of the tomato mixture down the center. Loosen the edges of the omelet with a spatula and fold the 2 sides over the filling. Slide out onto a warm plate. Repeat with the remaining ½ teaspoon oil, egg mixture, and tomato mixture.

Total time: 30 minutes ✴ Makes 2 servings

Per serving: 210 calories, 17 g protein, 8 g carbohydrates, 13 g total fat, 4 g saturated fat, 2 g fiber, 782 mg sodium

Egg protein is one of the most complete and digestible of all proteins. The 6 grams in each egg can help balance your blood sugar.

# Mixed Vegetable Sformato

2 pounds broccoli florets

4 tablespoons water, divided

2 teaspoons olive oil

½ small onion, chopped

4 ounces fresh mushrooms, sliced

1 clove garlic, minced

2 eggs

4 egg whites

⅔ cup panko bread crumbs

1 teaspoon salt

1 teaspoon pepper

**PREHEAT** the oven to 350°F. Coat a 9" × 5" × 3" loaf pan with cooking spray.

**IN** a medium microwaveable bowl, combine half of the broccoli and 2 tablespoons of the water. Microwave on high power for about 4 minutes, or until soft. Drain and remove the broccoli to a plate. Repeat with the remaining broccoli and 2 tablespoons water.

**HEAT** the oil in a medium skillet over medium-high heat. Cook the onion, mushrooms, and garlic for about 5 minutes, or until soft. Place in a food processor with half of the broccoli. Process for about 1 minute, or until almost smooth. Remove to a mixing bowl.

**TO** the food processor, add the eggs, egg whites, bread crumbs, salt, pepper, and the remaining broccoli. Process for about 1 minute, or until smooth. With a spatula, fold into the mushroom mixture. Scrape into the loaf pan.

**BAKE** for about 45 minutes, or until a wooden pick inserted in the center comes out clean.

**COOL** in the pan on a rack for 5 minutes. Place a platter over the pan. Using oven mitts, invert the pan to release the sformato. Cut into slices.

Total time: 1 hour 15 minutes ✳ Makes 6 servings

Per serving: 127 calories, 10 g protein, 17 g carbohydrates, 4 g total fat, 1 g saturated fat, 5 g fiber, 512 mg sodium

Broaden your cooking repertoire as you shrink your waistline. This recipe introduces you to an Italian vegetable flan called sformato (sfohr-MAH-toh), which is similar to a soufflé but not as airy.

# Baked Eggs with Cheese and Zucchini

4 teaspoons olive oil

2 zucchini or yellow squash (12 ounces), thinly sliced

½ small onion, chopped

½ teaspoon dried basil

½ teaspoon salt, divided

¼ teaspoon pepper, divided

¼ cup shredded sharp Provolone or Swiss cheese

8 eggs

1 tablespoon whole milk

**PREHEAT** the oven to 350°F. Coat a 13" × 9" baking dish with cooking spray.

**HEAT** the oil in a large nonstick skillet over medium heat. Cook the zucchini or squash, onion, basil, ¼ teaspoon of the salt, and ⅛ teaspoon of the pepper for 5 minutes, stirring frequently, or until tender-crisp.

**SPREAD** the mixture over the bottom of the baking dish. Sprinkle with 2 tablespoons of the cheese. With the back of a spoon, make 8 indentations in the mixture. Divide the eggs among the indentations. Sprinkle with the remaining ¼ teaspoon salt, ⅛ teaspoon pepper, and 2 tablespoons cheese. Drizzle with the milk.

**COVER** with foil and bake for about 20 minutes, or until the egg whites are set and the yolks begin to thicken.

---

Total time: 35 minutes  ✱  Makes 4 servings

Per serving: 243 calories, 16 g protein, 6 g carbohydrates, 18 g total fat, 7 g saturated fat, 2 g fiber, 519 mg sodium

**QUICK TIP: EGG-CELERATE YOUR WEIGHT LOSS**

400 The reduction in calories eaten all day after an egg-and-toast breakfast

# Garden Vegetable Wrap

4 spinach-flavored flour tortillas (12" diameter)

2 teaspoons olive oil

4 eggs

4 egg whites

½ cup crumbled reduced-fat lemon, garlic, and herb feta cheese

4 ounces baby arugula or baby spinach

Hot-pepper sauce (optional)

**PREHEAT** a grill pan over medium-high heat. Grill the tortillas, one at a time, for about 20 seconds, then flip and cook for 10 seconds, or until lightly toasted. Remove to a plate and cover with a slightly damp paper towel.

**HEAT** the oil in a large nonstick skillet over medium heat. In a mixing bowl, whisk together the eggs, egg whites, and cheese. Cook and stir for 2 minutes. Add the arugula or spinach. Cook and stir for about 1 minute, or until the eggs are set and the greens are wilted.

**DIVIDE** the tortillas among 4 plates. Divide the egg mixture in mounds on the bottom halves of the tortillas. Fold up the 2 sides and roll into tubes. Cut diagonally in half and serve with hot-pepper sauce (if using).

-------------------------------------------------------------

Total time: 10 minutes  ✱  Makes 4 servings

Per serving: 300 calories, 19 g protein, 33 g carbohydrates, 11 g total fat, 3 g saturated fat, 2 g fiber, 540 mg sodium

Versatile, portable, and packed with protein, wraps are ideal for a lean and healthy lifestyle.

# Ham and Vegetable Omelet Wrap

1 teaspoon canola oil

½ small onion, chopped

1½ ounces reduced-sodium sliced ham, chopped

¼ cup frozen baby peas

1 small plum tomato, chopped

⅛ teaspoon pepper

3 egg whites

1 egg

1 multigrain wrap (8" diameter)

4 teaspoons jarred black bean and corn salsa

**HEAT** the oil in a medium nonstick skillet over medium-high heat. Cook the onion and ham, stirring occasionally, for about 3 minutes, or until the onion starts to soften. Stir in the peas, tomato, and pepper. Cook for about 2 minutes, or until the tomato starts to soften.

**IN** a small bowl, lightly whisk together the egg whites and egg. Add to the pan. Cook and stir for about 4 minutes, or until set.

**WARM** the wrap according to package directions, then place on a cutting board. Slide the egg mixture onto the wrap, roll up jelly roll-style, then cut in half diagonally. Top with the salsa.

---

Total time: 20 minutes ✳ Makes 2 servings

Per serving: 171 calories, 16 g protein, 19 g carbohydrates, 6 g total fat, 2 g saturated fat, 3 g fiber, 450 mg sodium

If you're cooking for one, slip the extra serving into a resealable plastic bag (without the salsa), and you'll be set for breakfast tomorrow morning.

# Hearty Breakfast Egg Sandwich

1 egg

1 egg white

¼ avocado, mashed

1 whole grain English muffin, toasted

1 slice reduced-fat Cheddar cheese

2 slices tomato

**COAT** a small skillet with cooking spray. Heat over medium heat.

**IN** a small bowl, whisk together the egg and egg white. Pour into the pan. Cook and stir for about 4 minutes, or until set.

**SPREAD** the avocado on the muffin bottom. Top with the cheese, tomato, eggs, and muffin top.

---

Total time: 15 minutes ✻ Makes 1 serving

Per serving: 368 calories, 24 g protein, 34 g carbohydrates, 17 g total fat, 4 g saturated fat, 9 g fiber, 724 mg sodium

## QUICK TIP: BREATHE AWAY MORE FAT
Oxygen helps fuel your fat burn, so the more efficiently you breathe, the better your workout results. The trick: Breathe in and out through both your mouth and nose.

# Apple-Sausage Sauté

4 teaspoons olive oil, divided

1 pound precooked chicken or pork sausages, cut into ½" diagonal slices

4 medium Granny Smith apples, quartered, cut into ½" wedges

¼ teaspoon pepper

¼ teaspoon dried thyme

2 tablespoons maple syrup

**HEAT** 2 teaspoons of the oil in a large nonstick skillet over medium heat. Cook the sausages, turning often, for about 6 minutes, or until lightly browned. Remove to a plate.

**ADD** the remaining 2 teaspoons oil to the pan. Cook the apples, pepper, thyme, and syrup, tossing often, for about 12 minutes, or until the apples are tender. Add the sausages and toss for 1 minute to heat through.

----

Total time: 25 minutes ✻ Makes 4 servings

Per serving: 375 calories, 20 g protein, 45 g carbohydrates, 14 g total fat, 3 g saturated fat, 4 g fiber, 643 mg sodium

Any sensible approach to weight control includes moderate amounts of familiar fare such as sausages. Here, they're balanced with sweet, fiber-rich apples to bring down the total fat and calories.

# Hot Oatmeal with Blueberries, Cherries, and Brown Sugar

2 cups water

2 tablespoons packed light brown sugar

⅛ teaspoon salt

1 cup old-fashioned rolled oats

¼ cup dried tart cherries

½ cup blueberries

¼ teaspoon ground cinnamon

½ teaspoon vanilla extract

IN a small saucepan over medium-high heat, combine the water, sugar, and salt. Bring to a boil. Stir in the oats and cherries and reduce the heat to medium. Cook, stirring occasionally, for about 6 minutes, or until thickened. Remove from the heat and stir in the blueberries, cinnamon, and vanilla.

-------

Total time: 15 minutes  ✽  Makes 2 servings

Per serving: 290 calories, 8 g protein, 59 g carbohydrates, 3 g total fat, 0 g saturated fat, 9 g fiber, 157 mg sodium

Just as there are fans of cold pizza, some people like their oatmeal cool. Try cooking this fruity cereal the night before. Refrigerate it and you'll have a yummy pudding in the morning. Add a splash of milk or a dollop of Greek yogurt.

# Mixed Fruit Granola

3 cups old-fashioned rolled oats

¾ cup all-bran cereal

½ cup slivered almonds

1 teaspoon ground cinnamon

⅛ teaspoon ground nutmeg

¼ teaspoon salt

½ cup honey

3 tablespoons maple syrup

2 tablespoons canola oil

1 teaspoon almond extract

½ cup dried apricots, sliced

½ cup packed golden raisins

½ cup dried cranberries

PREHEAT the oven to 300°F. Coat a large baking sheet with cooking spray.

IN a large bowl, stir together the oats, cereal, almonds, cinnamon, nutmeg, and salt. In a small bowl, whisk together the honey, syrup, oil, and almond extract. Add to the oat mixture and toss well to combine. Spread evenly on the baking sheet.

BAKE, stirring every 10 minutes, for about 50 minutes, or until lightly toasted.

STIR in the apricots, raisins, and cranberries. Cool completely in the pan on a rack.

---

Total time: 1 hour 10 minutes  ✱  Makes 12 servings

Per serving: 232 calories, 5 g protein, 42 g carbohydrates, 6 g total fat, 0 g saturated fat, 5 g fiber, 61 mg sodium

For quick on-the-go breakfasts, whip up a batch and store in an airtight container in a cool spot for up to 2 weeks.

## QUICK TIP: C IS FOR CRANBERRY

20% The daily requirement for vitamin C in 1 cup of chopped cranberries

# Multigrain Cereal

1 cup old-fashioned rolled oats

1 cup wheat flakes

1 cup malted barley flakes

1 cup rye flakes

¾ cup ground flaxseed

½ pound dark or golden raisins

⅓ cup sesame seeds

IN a mixing bowl, stir together the oats, wheat flakes, barley flakes, rye flakes, flaxseed, raisins, and sesame seeds. Store in an airtight container in the freezer.

TO cook 1 serving: Bring 1 cup water and a pinch of salt to a boil in a small saucepan over high heat. Stir in ⅓ cup Multigrain Cereal. Reduce the heat to medium low. Cover and cook, stirring occasionally, for 25 minutes, or until thickened.

Total time: 30 minutes  ✽  Makes 18 servings

Per serving: 144 calories, 5 g protein, 27 g carbohydrates, 3 g total fat, 0 g saturated fat, 5 g fiber, 13 mg sodium

For convenience, cook a serving of cereal the night before and transfer to a microwaveable bowl. In the morning, stir in 2 tablespoons water. Cover and cook in the microwave for about 1 minute, or until heated.

# Banana Yogurt All-Bran Parfait

1 cup fat-free plain yogurt

1 cup all-bran cereal

1 banana, sliced

2 tablespoons honey

2 strawberries, stemmed

**DIVIDE** half of the yogurt between 2 parfait glasses. Divide ½ cup of the cereal, half of the banana, and 1 tablespoon of the honey between the glasses. Repeat with the remaining yogurt, cereal, and banana. Top with the strawberries and drizzle with the remaining 1 tablespoon honey.

Total time: 5 minutes  ✽  Makes 2 servings

Per serving: 271 calories, 12 g protein, 65 g carbohydrates, 2 g total fat, 0 g saturated fat, 11 g fiber, 171 mg sodium

Making visually satisfying dishes doesn't have to take a lot of effort. Admire the colorful layers as you savor the flavors of this easy breakfast.

# Western Cornbread

3 tablespoons canola oil

3 scallions, all parts, finely chopped

¼ red or yellow bell pepper, finely chopped

2 ounces Canadian bacon, finely chopped

1 cup yellow cornmeal

¾ cup whole grain pastry flour

½ cup all-purpose flour

2 teaspoons baking powder

1 teaspoon baking soda

¼ teaspoon salt

1 egg

1⅓ cups buttermilk

**PREHEAT** the oven to 425°F. Heat the oil in a 9" heavy skillet over medium-high heat for 30 seconds. Cook and stir the scallions, bell pepper, and bacon for about 1 minute, or until the scallions are wilted. Remove from the heat.

**IN** a mixing bowl, stir together the cornmeal, pastry flour, all-purpose flour, baking powder, baking soda, and salt. In a small bowl, whisk together the egg and buttermilk. Stir into the dry ingredients, just until no flour is visible. Stir in the bacon mixture. Pour into the skillet.

**BAKE** for about 15 minutes, or until a tester inserted in the center comes out clean. Serve warm.

-----

Total time: 30 minutes ✳ Makes 8 servings

Per serving: 211 calories, 7 g protein, 29 g carbohydrates, 8 g total fat, 1 g saturated fat, 3 g fiber, 510 mg sodium

Pair a steaming-hot-from-the-oven piece of this savory quick bread with a poached egg.

# Crunchy French Toast
# with Raspberry Fruit Spread

⅓ cup fat-free milk

1 egg

1 egg white

½ teaspoon vanilla extract

⅛ teaspoon ground cinnamon

4 slices oat-bran or whole wheat bread

¾ cup crushed all-fiber cereal

8 teaspoons raspberry all-fruit spread

PREHEAT the oven to 375°F. Coat a baking sheet with cooking spray.

IN a large shallow baking dish, whisk the milk, egg, egg white, vanilla, and cinnamon. Add the bread and soak until most of the liquid is absorbed. Place the cereal in a shallow dish. One at a time, dip the bread slices into the cereal to coat both sides. Place on the baking sheet.

BAKE for about 14 minutes, turning once, or until lightly browned on both sides. Top with the fruit spread.

Total time: 30 minutes  ✱  Makes 4 servings

Per serving: 146 calories, 7 g protein, 28 g carbohydrates, 3 g total fat, 1 g saturated fat, 6 g fiber, 207 mg sodium

## HEALTH HEARSAY

**Q. Are bottled teas a good source of antioxidants?**

**A.** You'd likely never drink 20 bottles of tea in a day—but that's how much you would have to sip of some brands to get the same amount of disease-fighting polyphenols as 1 cup of brewed tea. In a new study, researchers analyzed 49 brands of bottled tea and found that most had very low or no antioxidants. What they did have was plenty of sugar. So stick to tea bags, and if it's iced tea you want, brew your own and chill it right away to help preserve more antioxidants, says Shiming Li, PhD, lead author of the study. If you must add sweetener, go easy.

# Buttermilk Blueberry Pancakes

1¼ cups quick-cooking oats

½ cup whole grain pastry flour

3 tablespoons sugar

½ teaspoon baking powder

¼ teaspoon baking soda

⅛ teaspoon salt

1 cup buttermilk

1 egg

1 egg white

1 tablespoon canola oil

1 teaspoon grated lemon peel

1 cup blueberries

½ cup maple syrup

IN a large bowl, stir together the oats, flour, sugar, baking powder, baking soda, and salt.

IN a small bowl, whisk together the buttermilk, egg, egg white, oil, and lemon peel. Stir into the oat mixture until just moistened. Gently fold in the blueberries. Refrigerate for 30 minutes.

PREHEAT the oven to 250°F. Coat a large nonstick skillet with cooking spray. Heat over medium heat. Spoon four ¼ cupfuls of batter into the skillet and cook for 2 minutes, or until the tops begin to bubble slightly. Turn and cook for about 3 minutes, or until golden and cooked through. Transfer to a baking sheet and keep warm in the oven. Repeat with the remaining batter to make 12 pancakes in all. Divide the syrup over the pancakes.

Total time: 55 minutes  ✽  Makes 6 servings (2 pancakes per serving)

Per serving: 260 calories, 8 g protein, 50 g carbohydrates, 4 g total fat, 2 g saturated fat, 4 g fiber, 202 mg sodium

Perfect for brunch, these moist, light pancakes are filling, not fattening! Adding oatmeal to the batter is a delicious way to add fiber to your morning meal.

# Corn Griddle Cakes

⅔ cup whole grain pastry flour

⅔ cup yellow cornmeal

1 tablespoon sugar

1½ teaspoons baking powder

½ teaspoon baking soda

⅛ teaspoon pepper

1½ cups buttermilk or fat-free plain yogurt

1 egg

2 egg whites

2 tablespoons canola oil

1 cup fresh or frozen and thawed corn kernels

**PREHEAT** the oven to 200°F.

**IN** a large bowl, stir together the flour, cornmeal, sugar, baking powder, baking soda, and pepper.

**IN** a medium bowl, whisk together the buttermilk or yogurt, egg, egg whites, and oil until smooth. Fold in the corn. Stir into the dry ingredients.

**COAT** a griddle or large nonstick skillet with cooking spray. Heat over medium heat. For each pancake, spoon 3 tablespoons batter onto the griddle. Cook for about 3 minutes, or until the bottoms are golden brown. Turn and cook about 2 minutes more, or until browned. Transfer to a baking sheet. Keep warm in the oven while making the remaining pancakes. There will be 16 in all.

--------

Total time: 35 minutes  ✳  Makes 4 servings (4 cakes per serving)

Per serving: 307 calories, 11 g protein, 45 g carbohydrates, 10 g total fat, 2 g saturated fat, 4 g fiber, 457 mg sodium

Perfect for weekend breakfasts, tasty griddle quick breads are delicious served with avocado, salsa, and cilantro.

# Bran Cakes with Maple Mixed Berries

1 pint strawberries, thinly sliced

1 pint blackberries, halved

5 tablespoons maple syrup, divided

1 cup fat-free milk

¾ cup all-bran cereal

1 cup whole grain pastry flour

1 teaspoon baking powder

½ teaspoon baking soda

½ teaspoon ground cinnamon

¼ teaspoon salt

1 egg

2 tablespoons canola oil

PREHEAT the oven to 200°F.

IN a medium bowl, stir together the strawberries, blackberries, and 3 tablespoons of the syrup.

IN a medium bowl, stir together the milk and cereal. Let stand for 10 minutes, or until softened.

MEANWHILE, in a large bowl, stir together the flour, baking powder, baking soda, cinnamon, and salt.

IN a medium bowl, whisk together the egg, oil, the remaining 2 tablespoons syrup, and the cereal mixture. Stir into the dry ingredients until no flour is visible.

COAT a griddle or large nonstick skillet with cooking spray. Heat over medium-high heat. For each pancake, spoon 2 tablespoons batter onto the griddle. Cook for about 2 minutes, or until the bottoms are golden brown. Turn and cook for about 1 minute, or until browned. Remove to a baking sheet. Keep warm in the oven while making the remaining pancakes. There will be 16 in all. Divide the berries over the pancakes.

Total time: 42 minutes  ✱  Makes 4 servings (4 pancakes per serving)

Per serving: 338 calories, 10 g protein, 60 g carbohydrates, 10 g total fat, 1 g saturated fat, 11 g fiber, 478 mg sodium

Create your own convenience breakfasts from the freezer. Cool any leftover pancakes to room temperature, then place in a stack separated by small sheets of waxed paper. Pop into a resealable plastic bag and freeze. Reheat in a toaster or toaster oven.

# Cinnamon Waffles with Apricot Jam

1 cup whole grain flour

1 cup old-fashioned rolled oats

2 tablespoons sugar

1 tablespoon + 1 teaspoon baking powder

¾ teaspoon ground cinnamon

Pinch of salt

1¼ cups buttermilk

½ cup water

3 tablespoons canola oil

1 egg

½ cup all-fruit apricot jam, warmed

**PREHEAT** the waffle iron. Coat lightly with cooking spray.

**IN** a medium bowl, stir together the flour, oats, sugar, baking powder, cinnamon, and salt.

**IN** a large bowl, whisk together the buttermilk, water, oil, and egg. Stir into the flour mixture.

**DOLLOP** a generous ½ cup batter per waffle on the waffle iron and cook for about 5 minutes, or until browned and crisp. Repeat with the remaining batter, coating the griddle with cooking spray as needed.

**DIVIDE** the waffles among 4 plates. Top with the warmed jam.

-------------------------------------------------------------------

Total time: 15 minutes ✱ Makes 4 servings

Per serving: 355 calories, 11 g protein, 53 g carbohydrates, 14 g total fat, 2 g saturated fat, 4 g fiber, 412 mg sodium

For quick workday breakfasts, prepare the waffles on the weekend. Wrap them individually and freeze for up to 3 weeks. Reheat in a toaster oven on low heat until warmed through.

# Rhubarb Brunch Cake

1 pound rhubarb, chopped

½ cup granulated sugar

2 tablespoons cornstarch

2 cups all-purpose flour

2 teaspoons baking powder

2 teaspoons baking soda

¾ cup honey

¾ cup buttermilk

½ cup mashed banana

⅓ cup prune puree

¼ cup canola oil

1 egg

3 egg whites

⅓ cup packed light brown sugar

1 tablespoon chopped walnuts

**PREHEAT** the oven to 350°F. Coat a 13" × 9" baking pan with cooking spray.

**IN** a medium saucepan, stir together the rhubarb, granulated sugar, and cornstarch. Cook over medium heat, stirring frequently, for 10 minutes, or until the rhubarb is soft.

**MEANWHILE,** in a large bowl, stir together the flour, baking powder, and baking soda. In a medium bowl, whisk together the honey, buttermilk, banana, prune puree, oil, egg, and egg whites. Stir into the flour mixture until just blended.

**POUR** half of the batter into the baking pan. Smooth the top with a spatula. Top evenly with the rhubarb mixture. Top with the remaining batter. Smooth with a spatula. Sprinkle with the brown sugar and nuts.

**BAKE** for about 40 minutes, or until golden brown and a wooden pick inserted into the center comes out clean. Cool in the pan on a rack.

Total time: 1 hour  ✽  Makes 12 servings

Per serving: 359 calories, 6 g protein, 60 g carbohydrates, 12 g total fat, 1 g saturated fat, 3 g fiber, 324 mg sodium

Eating foods when they are in season locally is a great way to keep your diet interesting. Rhubarb, a member of the buckwheat family, is a sure sign of spring.

# Breakfast Fruit Crisp

4 peaches, sliced

¼ cup + 3 tablespoons packed light brown sugar

2 tablespoons + ½ cup whole grain pastry flour

1 tablespoon lemon juice

1 teaspoon pumpkin pie spice

1 cup raspberries

⅓ cup old-fashioned rolled oats

⅛ teaspoon salt

2 tablespoons butter, cut into small pieces

2 tablespoons reduced-fat sour cream

**PREHEAT** the oven to 400°F.

**IN** a microwaveable and ovenproof 9" baking dish or pie pan, stir together the peaches, ¼ cup of the sugar, 2 tablespoons of the flour, the lemon juice, and spice. Microwave on high power, stirring halfway through, for about 8 minutes, or until a sauce forms. Stir in the raspberries and spread in an even layer.

**IN** a medium bowl, stir together the oats, salt, the remaining 3 tablespoons brown sugar, and the remaining ½ cup flour. Cut in the butter until the mixture is crumbly. Stir in the sour cream until combined. Crumble evenly over the fruit.

**BAKE** for about 15 minutes, or until the topping is browned and the fruit is bubbly.

Total time: 35 minutes ✳ Makes 4 servings

Per serving: 308 calories, 5 g protein, 57 g carbohydrates, 8 g total fat, 4 g saturated fat, 5 g fiber, 126 mg sodium

With a rich, crunchy topping, this baked fruit dish will fool you into thinking you're eating dessert first thing in the morning.

# Apple Spice Coffee Cake

1½ cups white whole wheat flour or whole grain pastry flour

2 teaspoons baking powder

½ teaspoon baking soda

½ teaspoon ground cinnamon

¼ teaspoon ground ginger

½ cup packed light brown sugar

2 tablespoons trans-free spread or butter, softened

3 eggs

½ cup fat-free sour cream

2 apples, peeled and chopped

**PREHEAT** the oven to 350°F. Coat an 8" × 8" nonstick baking dish with cooking spray.

**IN** a medium bowl, stir together the flour, baking powder, baking soda, cinnamon, and ginger.

**IN** a medium bowl, beat together the sugar and spread or butter until smooth. Beat in the eggs and sour cream until blended. Beat in half of the flour mixture until blended, then beat in the remaining flour mixture for about 1 minute, or until the batter is smooth. Fold in the apples. Spread evenly in the baking dish.

**BAKE** for about 35 minutes, or until a wooden pick inserted in the center comes out clean.

**COOL** in the dish on a rack for 10 minutes. Serve warm or at room temperature.

Total time: 1 hour ✱ Makes 9 servings

Per serving: 181 calories, 5 g protein, 33 g carbohydrates, 4 g total fat, 1 g saturated fat, 2 g fiber, 244 mg sodium

Look for the new "white whole wheat flour" in your supermarket. It's ground from an albino strain of wheat kernels, so although it's lighter in color, it includes the nutritious bran, germ, and endosperm, just like regular whole wheat.

# Raisin Coffee Cake Ring with Orange Glaze

Coffee Cake

1½ cups raisins

½ cup orange juice

2 teaspoons vanilla extract

¼ teaspoon ground cinnamon

2 teaspoons trans-free spread or butter

1 pound frozen whole wheat or white bread dough, thawed

Glaze

3 tablespoons confectioners' sugar

2 tablespoons orange juice

1 teaspoon trans-free spread or butter

To make the cake:

**IN** a medium saucepan, stir together the raisins, orange juice, vanilla, and cinnamon. Cook over medium heat, stirring frequently, for about 6 minutes, or until the raisins have absorbed the liquid. Remove from the heat and stir in the spread or butter.

**COAT** a baking sheet with cooking spray. On a work surface, pat and stretch the dough into a 12" × 6" rectangle.

**SPREAD** evenly with the raisin mixture, leaving about ½" uncovered along 1 long side. Starting with the other long side, roll the dough tightly. Pinch the edges together to seal.

**TRANSFER** the dough to the baking sheet, forming it into a ring. Pinch the ends together. Use a sharp knife to cut into the ring at 12 intervals about 1½" apart (cut almost but not all the way through the ring). Spread the cuts out slightly so the filling is visible.

**COVER** loosely with plastic wrap and set aside in a warm spot for about 1½ hours, or until doubled in bulk.

**PREHEAT** the oven to 350°F.

**BAKE** for about 25 minutes, or until golden. Cool on the pan on a rack for about 10 minutes.

To make the glaze:

**IN** a small microwaveable bowl, combine the confectioners' sugar, orange juice, and spread or butter. Microwave on high power for about 30 seconds, or until the butter melts. Whisk until smooth. Drizzle over the coffee cake.

---

Total time: 2 hours 30 minutes ✱ Makes 12 servings

Per serving: 176 calories, 5 g protein, 36 g carbohydrates, 3 g total fat, 1 g saturated fat, 2 g fiber, 214 mg sodium

Making this comforting, old-fashioned pastry is super easy when you start with refrigerated dough.

# Pear Almond Muffins

1½ cups whole grain pastry flour

¾ cup wheat bran

¼ cup ground almonds

¼ cup sugar

1¼ teaspoons baking soda

¼ teaspoon salt

1¼ cups buttermilk

2 eggs

3 tablespoons canola oil

2 teaspoons almond extract

1 Bosc pear, finely chopped

**PREHEAT** the oven to 350°F. Coat a 12-cup muffin pan with cooking spray.

**IN** a large mixing bowl, stir together the flour, bran, almonds, sugar, baking soda, and salt. In another mixing bowl, whisk together the buttermilk, eggs, oil, and almond extract. Make a well in the center of the dry ingredients. Add the wet ingredients and the pear. Mix just to combine. Divide the batter evenly among the muffin cups.

**BAKE** for 20 minutes, or until golden and a wooden pick inserted in the center comes out clean. Cool in the pan on a rack for 10 minutes. Remove to the rack and cool completely.

-----

Total time: 40 minutes ✱ Makes 12

Per muffin: 140 calories, 4 g protein, 19 g carbohydrates, 6 g total fat, 1 g saturated fat, 3 g fiber, 220 mg sodium

Greet the day with the delightful flavor combination of pears and almonds. These muffins freeze well, so you can heat one in the toaster oven or microwave oven and be on your way.

# Zucchini-Raisin Muffins

½ cup canola oil

½ cup honey

2 eggs

1 teaspoon vanilla extract

1 cup whole grain pastry flour or all-purpose flour

¼ cup toasted wheat germ

1 teaspoon ground cinnamon

½ teaspoon baking powder

½ teaspoon baking soda

½ teaspoon salt

1 cup shredded zucchini

½ cup raisins

**PREHEAT** the oven to 350°F. Coat a 12-cup muffin pan with cooking spray.

**IN** a small bowl, whisk together the oil, honey, eggs, and vanilla.

**IN** a large bowl, stir together the flour, wheat germ, cinnamon, baking powder, baking soda, and salt. Make a well in the center and stir in the egg mixture just until combined. Fold in the zucchini and raisins. Divide evenly among the muffin cups.

**BAKE** for about 25 minutes, or until a wooden pick inserted in the center comes out clean. Cool in the pan on a rack for 5 minutes. Remove to the rack and cool completely.

Total time: 45 minutes  ✳  Makes 12

Per muffin: 199 calories, 4 g protein, 25 g carbohydrates, 10 g total fat, 1 g saturated fat, 2 g fiber, 184 mg sodium

For a colorful variation, replace the zucchini with yellow summer squash and the raisins with dried cranberries.

# Rolled Biscuits

2 cups whole grain pastry flour or all-purpose flour

2½ teaspoons baking powder

½ teaspoon baking soda

3 tablespoons trans-free spread or butter

⅔ cup buttermilk

**PREHEAT** the oven to 425°F. Coat a nonstick baking sheet with cooking spray.

**IN** a medium bowl, stir together the flour, baking powder, and baking soda. Using 2 table knives or a pastry blender, cut in the spread or butter until coarse crumbs form. Gently stir in the buttermilk until a dough forms. Turn the dough out onto a lightly floured surface and gently knead for 1 minute.

**WITH** a floured rolling pin or floured hands, gently roll or pat the dough into a ½"-thick rectangle. With a 2" round cutter, cut the dough into rounds, rerolling as needed to cut 12. Remove to the baking sheet. Lightly coat the tops with cooking spray.

**BAKE** for about 12 minutes, or until lightly golden.

---

Total time: 30 minutes ✽ Makes 12

Per biscuit: 84 calories, 2 g protein, 13 g carbohydrates, 3 g total fat, 1 g saturated fat, 2 g fiber, 204 mg sodium

Whole grain pastry flour is milled very fine, so it produces tender pastry. Most supermarkets stock it in the baking aisle or natural foods section.

# Walnut Lemon Scones

1 cup whole grain pastry flour or all-purpose flour

2 tablespoons sugar

2 teaspoons baking powder

½ teaspoon ground cinnamon

¼ teaspoon baking soda

¼ teaspoon salt

½ cup cold trans-free spread or butter, cut into bits

¼ cup buttermilk

1 egg

½ teaspoon grated lemon peel

¼ teaspoon lemon extract

⅓ cup chopped walnuts, toasted (see note page 98)

PREHEAT the oven to 400°F. Lightly coat a baking sheet with cooking spray.

IN a large bowl, stir together the flour, sugar, baking powder, cinnamon, baking soda, and salt. With a pastry blender or 2 knives, cut the spread or butter into the dry ingredients until the mixture resembles coarse meal. In a small bowl, whisk together the buttermilk, egg, lemon peel, and lemon extract. Stir into the dry ingredients along with the walnuts to form a moist dough. Using wet hands, knead the dough 4 or 5 times in the bowl. Place the dough onto the baking sheet and form into a ¾"-thick disk. Cut the disk all the way through into 8 wedges, but don't separate them.

BAKE for about 16 minutes, or until lightly golden. Cool on the pan on a rack for about 10 minutes. Serve warm or at room temperature.

---

Total time: 40 minutes ✱ Makes 8

Per scone: 177 calories, 3 g protein, 11 g carbohydrates, 13 g total fat, 3 g saturated fat, 2 g fiber, 356 mg sodium

Unlike regular scones that are packed with calories and fat from butter, these smarter pastries get their flakiness from naturally low-fat buttermilk.

# Orange, Grapefruit, and Kiwifruit with Toasted Almonds

3 navel oranges, cut into sections

1 large red grapefruit, cut into sections

3 kiwifruit, halved and sliced

2 tablespoons dried cherries or cranberries

2 tablespoons slivered almonds, toasted (see note)

IN a mixing bowl, stir together the oranges, grapefruit, kiwi, and cherries or cranberries. Divide among 4 bowls and top with the nuts.

----

Total time: 10 minutes  ✱  Makes 4 servings

Per serving: 143 calories, 3 g protein, 32 g carbohydrates, 2 g total fat, 0 g saturated fat, 6 g fiber, 4 mg sodium

This refreshing compote packs one-third of your recommended fruit intake for the entire day.

Toast nuts to crisp the texture and bring out the flavor. Spread nuts on a dry baking sheet. Bake in a preheated 325°F oven, stirring occasionally, for about 10 minutes, or until sizzling. The toasting time will vary, depending on the type of nut and whether it is whole or chopped. Let stand to cool. You can toast 1 or 2 cups of nuts at one time, then cool and store in an airtight container in a cool spot for several weeks.

# Stewed Winter Fruits

2 cups mixed dried fruit, coarsely chopped

1½ cups orange juice

½ cup water

2 tablespoons packed light brown sugar

⅛ teaspoon ground cinnamon

2 tablespoons chopped walnuts, toasted (see note opposite page)

2 teaspoons vanilla extract

IN a medium saucepan, stir together the dried fruit, orange juice, water, sugar, and cinnamon. Cook over medium-high heat, stirring occasionally, for about 5 minutes, or until boiling and the sugar is dissolved. Reduce the heat to medium and cook, stirring occasionally, for 15 minutes, or until the liquid is reduced to a thick syrup. Stir in the walnuts and vanilla.

Total time: 25 minutes ✱ Makes 6 servings

Per serving: 230 calories, 2 g protein, 48 g carbohydrates, 2 g total fat, 0 g saturated fat, 3 g fiber, 135 mg sodium

This comforting dried-fruit combo can also be enjoyed as a snack with a dollop of 0% plain Greek yogurt.

# Minted Honey-Lime Fruit Salad

¼ cup honey

2 tablespoons lime juice

3 tablespoons chopped fresh mint

1 teaspoon grated lime peel

½ small honeydew, cubed

½ cantaloupe, cubed

1 pint fresh strawberries, halved

½ pineapple, cubed, or 1 can (20 ounces) pineapple chunks in juice, drained

IN a large bowl, whisk together the honey, lime juice, mint, and lime peel until the honey dissolves. Stir in the honeydew, cantaloupe, strawberries, and pineapple.

--------

Total time: 10 minutes ✳ Makes 8 servings

Per serving: 97 calories, 1 g protein, 25 g carbohydrates, 0 g total fat, 0 g saturated fat, 2 g fiber, 21 mg sodium

Melon is naturally sweet and bursting with water—a great food for filling up with few calories.

# Blueberry-Pomegranate Smoothie

⅔ cup frozen blueberries

½ cup fat-free French vanilla yogurt

⅓ cup vanilla soy milk

¼ cup pomegranate juice

**IN** a blender, combine the blueberries, yogurt, soy milk, and pomegranate juice. Blend for about 2 minutes, or until smooth.

---

Total time: 5 minutes ✳ Makes 1 serving

Per serving: 227 calories, 9 g protein, 45 g carbohydrates, 2 g total fat, 0 g saturated fat, 3 g fiber, 123 mg sodium

A dash of warming ground cinnamon adds spark to this quick morning beverage.

**QUICK TIP: GOODNESS GRAPEFRUIT**

76% The daily requirement for vitamin C found in half a grapefruit

# Watermelon Smoothie

1 large slice watermelon, chopped (2 cups)

¼ cup fat-free milk

2 cups crushed ice

**IN** a blender, combine the watermelon and milk. Blend for 15 seconds, or until smooth. Add the ice. Blend for about 20 seconds, or until thickened.

Total time: 5 minutes ✱ Makes 2 servings

Per serving: 56 calories, 2 g protein, 13 g carbohydrates, 0 g total fat, 0 g saturated fat, 1 g fiber, 20 mg sodium

As part of a summertime breakfast, what could be more refreshing than a watermelon smoothie?

# Tutti-Frutti Smoothie

½ cup loose-pack mixed frozen berries or strawberries

½ cup canned crushed pineapple in juice

½ cup fat-free plain yogurt

½ very ripe banana, sliced

½ cup orange juice

IN a blender, combine the berries, pineapple, yogurt, banana, and orange juice. Blend for about 2 minutes, or until smooth.

Total time: 5 minutes ✻ Makes 2 servings

Per serving: 140 calories, 7 g protein, 29 g carbohydrates, 0 g total fat, 0 g saturated fat, 3 g fiber, 29 mg sodium

Boost your daily fruit intake with this creamy concoction.

# lunches

# Open-Faced Peppered Steak Sandwiches

- 1 pound beef flank steak, trimmed of all visible fat
- ½ cup balsamic vinegar
- 1 teaspoon pepper
- 2 onions, chopped
- ¼ cup reduced-sodium chicken broth
- 1 loaf French bread (about 8 ounces)
- 1 teaspoon olive oil
- 2 cloves garlic, minced

**PLACE** the steak and vinegar in a large resealable plastic bag. Massage to coat evenly. Refrigerate for 1 hour, turning occasionally.

**REMOVE** the steak and discard the vinegar. Pat the steak dry and rub with the pepper.

**IN** a medium nonstick skillet over medium-high heat, combine the onions and broth. Bring to a boil. Reduce the heat to medium-low and cook for 10 minutes, or until soft. Increase the heat to high. Cook and stir for 3 minutes, or until golden brown. Remove to a plate.

**REDUCE** the heat to medium-high. Cook the steak for 7 minutes, or until browned. Turn and cook for about 8 minutes, or until a thermometer inserted in the center registers 145°F for medium-rare/160°F for medium/165°F for well-done. Let stand for 10 minutes before thinly slicing crosswise.

**MEANWHILE,** preheat the oven to 400°F. Split the bread in half lengthwise. Brush the cut sides with the oil. Place the bread, cut side up, on a baking sheet. Bake for 5 minutes, or until golden brown. Cut each half into 4 pieces. Divide the garlic, onions, and steak on the bread.

Total time: 1 hour 40 minutes  ✱  Makes 8 servings

Per serving: 218 calories, 17 g protein, 27 g carbohydrates, 4 g total fat, 2 g saturated fat, 2 g fiber, 302 mg sodium

Prepare this hearty luncheon dish ahead of time for quick reheating. To freeze, pack the cooled cooked steak in a freezer-quality bag. Pack the onions separately. To eat, thaw and reheat in the microwave oven.

## NUTRITION NEWS TO USE
## BURGER + FROZEN YOGURT = FLUSH FAT
The next time you eat a food high in saturated fat, follow it with a low-fat, calcium-rich dessert. Calcium binds to fatty acids in the digestive tract, blocking their absorption. In one study, participants who took in 1,735 milligrams of calcium from low-fat dairy products (about as much as in five 8-ounce glasses of fat-free milk) blocked the equivalent of 85 calories a day.

# Better Beef Burgers

½ small onion, finely chopped

1½ ounces fresh mushrooms, finely chopped

1½ tablespoons chopped fresh parsley or thyme

1 tablespoon reduced-sodium Worcestershire sauce

¼ teaspoon hot-pepper sauce

¾ pound extra-lean ground beef

4 kaiser rolls, toasted

4 leaves lettuce

4 slices tomato

**COAT** a medium nonstick skillet with cooking spray. Heat over medium heat. Cook the onion and mushrooms, stirring occasionally, for about 5 minutes, or until the mushrooms are lightly browned. Remove to a medium bowl. Stir in the parsley or thyme, Worcestershire sauce, and hot-pepper sauce. Add the beef and mix quickly with your hands to combine. Shape into 4 burgers.

**COAT** a grill rack with cooking spray. Preheat the grill to medium-high. Place the rack on the grill.

**GRILL** the burgers for about 5 minutes per side, or until a thermometer inserted in the center registers 160°F and the meat is no longer pink. Divide the burgers, topped with the lettuce and tomatoes, among the rolls.

---

Total time: 25 minutes ✽ Makes 4 servings

Per serving: 279 calories, 23 g protein, 33 g carbohydrates, 6 g total fat, 2 g saturated fat, 2 g fiber, 375 mg sodium

Mixing mushrooms into the beef cuts the fat and calories while boosting the moistness and flavor.

## NUTRITION NEWS TO USE

Red meat lovers, rejoice—a twice-weekly steak dinner won't cause a heart attack. But keep careful tabs on your intake of bacon, sausage, and processed red meats. In a Harvard School of Public Health review, the risk of developing heart disease was 42 percent higher for every 1.8 ounces of processed meat eaten daily—that's about two slices of deli meat or a hot dog. Processed red meat can contain four times as much sodium and twice as many nitrates as unprocessed, contributing to high blood pressure and atherosclerosis. Researchers suggest limiting your intake of processed meat to one serving weekly.

# Barbecued Chicken Sandwiches

1 can (14.5 ounces) reduced-sodium chicken broth

1 can (8 ounces) no-salt-added crushed tomatoes

1 small onion, finely chopped

2 tablespoons apple cider vinegar

2 tablespoons packed light brown sugar

1 tablespoon Worcestershire sauce

2 teaspoons mustard powder or 1 teaspoon Dijon mustard

1 pound boneless, skinless chicken breasts

4 whole grain hamburger buns

Hot-pepper sauce

**IN** a medium skillet, stir together the broth, tomatoes, onion, vinegar, sugar, Worcestershire sauce, and mustard. Bring to a boil over medium-high heat. Reduce the heat to low and add the chicken. Cover and simmer for 30 minutes, or until the chicken is very tender.

**WITH** a slotted spoon, remove the chicken to a cutting board. Let stand for about 10 minutes. Continue cooking the sauce, uncovered, for about 12 minutes, or until reduced by half. With 2 forks, shred the chicken. Return to the pan and stir to coat evenly with sauce.

**COOK** over low heat for about 3 minutes, or until warm. Divide the chicken and sauce among the buns. Season to taste with hot-pepper sauce.

--------------------------------------------------

Total time: 1 hour &#10042; Makes 4 servings

Per serving: 310 calories, 30 g protein, 35 g carbohydrates, 5 g total fat, 1 g saturated fat, 5 g fiber, 635 mg sodium

This Southern favorite gains even more flavor if it's cooked ahead and refrigerated for a couple of days. Reheat gently in a saucepan or in the microwave oven.

# Turkey Tacos with Avocado-Corn Salsa

1 avocado, chopped

1 cup fresh or frozen and thawed corn kernels

1 cup cherry tomatoes, halved

1 tablespoon lime juice

1 package (12) corn taco shells

¾ pound cooked boneless, skinless turkey breast, thinly sliced

¾ cup water

1 package (1¼ ounces) reduced-sodium taco seasoning mix

IN a medium bowl, stir together the avocado, corn, tomatoes, and lime juice.

WARM the shells according to package directions.

IN a medium skillet, stir together the turkey, water, and seasoning. Bring to a boil over medium-high heat. Reduce the heat to medium-low and cook, stirring occasionally, for 5 minutes, or until heated through.

DIVIDE the turkey mixture among the shells. Top with the avocado-corn salsa.

------

Total time: 15 minutes ✱ Makes 6 servings

Per serving: 310 calories, 21 g protein, 31 g carbohydrates, 12 g total fat, 2 g saturated fat, 5 g fiber, 524 mg sodium

Lean turkey breast keeps the fat and calories in check with these tasty tacos. Replace the turkey with chicken if you like.

# Herbed Chicken Sandwiches

- ½ pound boneless, skinless chicken breast
- ½ cup low-fat mayonnaise
- 1 teaspoon lemon juice
- 4 teaspoons chopped fresh dill or ½ teaspoon dried
- 12 thin slices multigrain bread
- ⅓ English cucumber, thinly sliced
- 1 large tomato, cut into 8 slices
- 1 cup mesclun or spring mix salad greens

**PLACE** a steamer basket or wire rack in a saucepan with 2" water. Bring to a boil over high heat. Steam the chicken in the basket or rack for about 10 minutes, or until a thermometer inserted in the thickest portion registers 165°F and the juices run clear. Remove from the basket or rack to a cutting board.

**MEANWHILE,** in a small bowl, stir together the mayonnaise, lemon juice, and dill. Toast the bread lightly.

**PLACE** the bread slices on a work surface. Divide the mayonnaise mixture evenly on the tops of all the slices. Thinly slice the chicken and divide evenly among 4 of the bread slices. Top with the cucumber and 4 more bread slices, mayonnaise side up. Top with the tomato, greens, and the remaining 4 bread slices, mayonnaise side down. Cut in half diagonally and secure with wooden picks.

------

Total time: 15 minutes ✳ Makes 4 servings

Per serving: 236 calories, 10 g protein, 37 g carbohydrates, 7 g total fat, 2 g saturated fat, 4 g fiber, 598 mg sodium

A lighter variation of a classic club sandwich made with bacon, this version is chock-full of fresh goodness from cucumber, tomato, and mixed greens.

# Hot Open-Faced
# Turkey Cheddar Sandwiches

4 slices rye bread

2 teaspoons Dijon mustard

4 boneless, skinless turkey breast cutlets (4 ounces each)

Pinch of salt

Pinch of black pepper

1 teaspoon olive oil

1 roasted red bell pepper, quartered

4 slices reduced-fat white Cheddar cheese (¾ ounce each)

**PREHEAT** the broiler. Lay the bread on a baking sheet. Spread the slices evenly with the mustard.

**LIGHTLY** pound each cutlet to an even thickness. Season with the salt and black pepper.

**HEAT** the oil in a large nonstick skillet over medium heat. Cook the turkey for about 5 minutes per side, or until a thermometer inserted in the thickest portion registers 165°F and the juices run clear. Remove from the heat.

**DIVIDE** the bell pepper, cutlets, and cheese among the bread slices. Broil for about 2 minutes, or until the cheese bubbles and lightly browns.

Total time: 15 minutes  ✱  Makes 4 servings

Per serving: 270 calories, 37 g protein, 17 g carbohydrates, 6 g total fat, 3 g saturated fat, 1 g fiber, 541 mg sodium

Making a sandwich with 1 slice of bread instead of 2 is a great way to slash the calories and keep sodium lower.

## [ METABOLISM BOOSTER: TRY RYE ]

Reach for genuine rye bread with caraway seeds for your next sandwich. The seeded bread has been shown to ease constipation 41 percent faster than drugs because it's high in the fiber arabinoxylan.

# Tuna Antipasto Sandwiches

4 ounces green beans, trimmed and cut into 1" pieces

2 tablespoons basil pesto

1 teaspoon white wine vinegar

1 loaf (12 ounces) whole grain peasant bread

1 can (12 ounces) water-packed chunk light tuna, drained and flaked

1 tomato, sliced

2 hard-cooked eggs, sliced

8 niçoise olives, pitted and sliced

BRING a medium skillet filled with 1" water to a boil over high heat. Add the beans and return to a boil. Cook for about 2 minutes, or until tender-crisp. Drain and then rinse under very cold water. Drain again and pat dry.

IN a small bowl, stir together the pesto and vinegar.

SLICE the bread in half horizontally and tear out the interior, leaving a ½" shell in each half (use the leftover bread to make bread crumbs). Layer the tuna, tomato, eggs, beans, and olives in the bottom bread shell. Drizzle with the pesto mixture. Top with the remaining bread shell. Wrap tightly with plastic wrap.

SET a heavy skillet on the sandwich. Let it sit for 30 minutes at room temperature.

CUT into wedges.

---

Total time: 45 minutes   ✱   Makes 4 servings

Per serving: 354 calories, 29 g protein, 39 g carbohydrates, 11 g total fat, 2 g saturated fat, 14 g fiber, 762 mg sodium

Pressing the sandwich for 30 minutes allows time for the pesto dressing to moisten the bread. For a version you can eat right away, sprinkle the bread shell lightly with ice water before filling.

# California Veggie Sandwich

2 tablespoons balsamic vinegar

1 clove garlic, minced

1 thick slice (3 ounces) firm tofu

½ teaspoon olive oil

1 tablespoon finely chopped almonds

2 slices low-calorie, high-fiber multigrain bread, lightly toasted

1 tablespoon shredded reduced-fat Cheddar cheese

⅙ avocado, peeled and sliced

2 slices tomato

IN a shallow bowl, stir together the vinegar and garlic. Place the tofu in the bowl. Marinate, turning occasionally, for 10 minutes.

REMOVE the tofu and pat dry. Drizzle with the oil and rub to coat the surface. Scatter the almonds evenly over the tofu, pressing to adhere.

COAT a medium nonstick skillet with cooking spray. Heat over medium heat. Cook the tofu for about 4 minutes per side, or until well browned. Remove to a bread slice. Top with the cheese, avocado, tomato, and the remaining bread slice.

---

Total time: 20 minutes  ✳  Makes 1 serving

Per serving: 340 calories, 16 g protein, 35 g carbohydrates, 17 g total fat, 3 g saturated fat, 9 g fiber, 310 mg sodium

Incorporating tofu and other soy foods is a smart way to cut saturated fat in your diet. Tofu is versatile because it absorbs flavors so well.

## GOTTA TRY IT: HEALTHY SANDWICH SPREAD

For a spread that's good for your heart, blend oil and vinegar with beans, says Brendan Brazier, the author of *Thrive*. In a blender, puree about three parts vinaigrette with one part cooked legumes. Adjust the amounts until the blend reaches your desired consistency. The spread also provides fiber, protein, good fats, iron, and folate, and it can be used as a dip for veggies and pitas or a sauce for pizza or pasta.

# Roasted Eggplant and Spinach Sandwiches

1 small eggplant, thickly sliced

1 red bell pepper, quartered

1 tomato, halved

1 small onion, thickly sliced

2 tablespoons olive oil

2 cloves garlic, minced

½ teaspoon crushed dried rosemary

1 round loaf Italian bread (8" diameter)

2 tablespoons fat-free plain yogurt

3 tablespoons balsamic vinegar

2 teaspoons grated Parmesan cheese

½ cup tightly packed spinach leaves

**PREHEAT** the oven to 400°F. Coat a large baking sheet with cooking spray.

**ARRANGE** the eggplant, pepper, tomato, and onion on the sheet. Brush with the oil. Sprinkle with the garlic and rosemary. Bake for 45 minutes, turning occasionally, or until golden brown and tender.

**SPLIT** the bread horizontally and scoop out the interior, leaving a 1" shell. (Reserve the bread for another use.) Spread the yogurt over the bottom of the shell and sprinkle with the vinegar. Top with the roasted vegetables, cheese, spinach, and bread top. Wrap tightly in plastic wrap and refrigerate for at least 30 minutes, or until chilled.

**CUT** into 8 wedges.

----

Total time: 1 hour 20 minutes  ✱  Makes 8 servings

Per serving: 220 calories, 7 g protein, 36 g carbohydrates, 6 g total fat, 1 g saturated fat, 4 g fiber, 346 mg sodium

Take a cue from the heart-healthy Mediterranean diet and lunch on hearty vegetables seasoned with olive oil and garlic.

# Grilled Tomato and Cheese Sandwiches

8 slices multigrain bread

8 slices low-fat Jarlsberg or Cheddar cheese

1 large tomato, cut into 8 slices

2 roasted red bell peppers, halved

12 large leaves fresh basil

COAT both sides of the bread with cooking spray. In a large nonstick skillet over medium heat, cook the bread on 1 side for 2 minutes, or until lightly toasted. Do this in batches, if necessary. Remove to a cutting board, toasted side up.

DIVIDE the cheese, tomato, peppers, and basil among 4 slices. Top with the remaining slices, toasted side down.

CAREFULLY place the sandwiches in the pan and cook over medium heat for 2 minutes per side, or until toasted and the cheese melts.

---

Total time: 10 minutes  ✱  Makes 4 servings

Per serving: 302 calories, 23 g protein, 37 g carbohydrates, 8 g total fat, 3 g saturated fat, 8 g fiber, 652 mg sodium

Everyone's favorite grilled cheese just got better with the addition of juicy tomato, mellow roasted bell pepper, and aromatic fresh basil.

# Mushroom-Onion Pizza

1 tablespoon olive oil

4 ounces fresh mushrooms, sliced

1 onion, sliced

1 package (15–16 ounces) refrigerated whole grain pizza dough

½ cup pasta sauce

1 cup grated part-skim mozzarella cheese

¼ cup grated Parmesan cheese

**PREHEAT** the oven to 450°F.

**HEAT** the oil in a large skillet over medium-high heat. Combine the mushrooms and onion in the skillet. Cover and cook for 3 minutes, or until sizzling. Remove the cover and cook for 5 minutes, or until almost all the liquid is gone.

**ON** a large, lightly floured baking sheet, pat the dough into a ¼" sheet. Spread on the sauce and sprinkle with the mozzarella, Parmesan, mushrooms, and onion.

**BAKE** for about 25 minutes, or until the crust is lightly browned and the cheese is bubbly.

Total time: 45 minutes ✳ Makes 4 servings

Per serving: 382 calories, 19 g protein, 55 g carbohydrates, 12 g total fat, 4 g saturated fat, 9 g fiber, 937 mg sodium

Starting with refrigerated dough makes this home-baked pie a cinch to prepare. It's a streamlined alternative to greasy carryout.

# Spinach-Cheese Enchiladas

2 cups reduced-sodium vegetable broth

2 cans (4.5 ounces each) chopped green chile peppers

2 tomatoes, chopped

2 scallions, all parts, finely chopped

2 cloves garlic, minced

2 tablespoons cornstarch

2 tablespoons water

1¼ pounds fresh spinach, coarsely chopped

½ cup shredded reduced-fat Monterey Jack cheese

8 corn tortillas (6" diameter)

**PREHEAT** the oven to 400°F. Coat a 13" × 9" nonstick baking dish with cooking spray.

**IN** a medium saucepan, stir together the broth, peppers, tomatoes, scallions, and garlic. Bring to a boil over high heat. Reduce the heat to medium and simmer for 15 minutes, or until the tomatoes are very soft.

**IN** a glass measuring cup, whisk together the cornstarch and water. Stir into the tomato mixture until thickened. Remove from the heat.

**MEANWHILE,** place the spinach in a large saucepan with about 2 tablespoons water. Cover and steam over medium heat for 2 minutes, or until wilted. Divide the spinach and cheese evenly among the tortillas. Roll up to enclose the filling.

**PLACE** the enchiladas, seam side down, in the baking dish. Top with the tomato mixture. Bake for 10 minutes, or until the filling is hot.

Total time: 35 minutes ✳ Makes 4 servings

Per serving: 241 calories, 12 g protein, 40 g carbohydrates, 6 g total fat, 2 g saturated fat, 9 g fiber, 630 mg sodium

## SUPERFOOD SPOTLIGHT: SPINACH

**Taste It:** Greens thrive in cool weather, so local spinach is the most flavorful and affordable from September to October and March to May.

**Love It:** Popeye was right. Spinach is a nutrition powerhouse, loaded with vitamins, antioxidants, and essential nutrients. It's one of the healthiest foods in the world, topping most other vegetables.

**Store It:** Keep spinach in the crisper drawer, loosely wrapped in paper towels and tucked in a plastic bag (just folded shut, not sealed).

# Fast-and-Easy Personal Chicken Pizza

1 whole wheat pita (6" diameter)

2 ounces sliced grilled or roasted chicken breast

1 small tomato, chopped

1 small clove garlic, minced

Dried oregano

¼ cup shredded part-skim mozzarella cheese

**PREHEAT** the broiler.

**PLACE** the pita on a small baking sheet. Broil for about 1 minute, or until golden. Top with the chicken, tomato, garlic, and a sprinkling of oregano. Sprinkle evenly with the cheese. Broil for about 2 minutes, or until the cheese is bubbly.

---

Total time: 10 minutes ✽ Makes 1 serving

Per serving: 300 calories, 33 g protein, 29 g carbohydrates, 8 g total fat, 2 g saturated fat, 10 g fiber, 430 mg sodium

For a zestier pizza, replace the part-skim mozzarella cheese with reduced-fat provolone cheese.

# Pizza Primavera

2 whole wheat pitas
(6" diameter)

1 teaspoon olive oil

1 cup reduced-sodium tomato
sauce

¼ cup chopped broccoli florets

¼ cup frozen artichoke hearts,
thawed and chopped

¼ cup chopped red bell pepper

½ small onion, chopped

1 teaspoon dried Italian herb
seasoning

1 cup shredded part-skim
mozzarella cheese

**PREHEAT** the oven to 400°F.

**SPLIT** the pitas horizontally into 4 disks. Place, inner side up, on a large baking sheet. Brush with the oil. Top evenly with the sauce, broccoli, artichokes, pepper, and onion. Sprinkle with the seasoning and cheese.

**BAKE** for 15 minutes, or until the cheese is bubbling.

---

Total time: 20 minutes ❋ Makes 4 servings

Per serving: 219 calories, 13 g protein, 27 g carbohydrates, 7 g total fat, 3 g saturated fat, 6 g fiber, 613 mg sodium

A bowl of Manhattan Clam Chowder (page 146) is a great companion to this pizza.

**[ QUICK TIP: MAKE IT QUICKER**
When you need a small quantity of chopped vegetables, hit the salad bar for ready-prepped ingredients. Buy just what you need—no waste! **]**

# Green Chile–Bean Burritos

1 cup instant brown rice

1 can (11.5 ounces) no-salt-added pinto beans, rinsed and drained

¾ cup green salsa

2 tablespoons lime juice

¼ cup chopped fresh cilantro

4 whole wheat tortillas (8" diameter)

½ cup shredded reduced-fat Monterey Jack Colby cheese

½ avocado, sliced

PREHEAT the oven to 350°F. Coat a baking pan with cooking spray.

COOK the rice according to package directions.

MEANWHILE, in a saucepan or skillet over medium heat, cook and stir the beans and salsa for about 3 minutes, or until warmed through. Remove from the heat. Add the lime juice, cilantro, and rice.

HEAT the tortillas according to package directions and place on a work surface. Sprinkle the cheese evenly down the center of the tortillas. Top with the avocado and the rice mixture. Fold the sides of the tortillas over the filling and roll up. Place on the baking pan, seam side down.

BAKE, turning once, for 15 minutes, or until golden and heated through.

---

Total time: 30 minutes  ✳  Makes 4 servings

Per serving: 372 calories, 14 g protein, 59 g carbohydrates, 9 g total fat, 2 g saturated fat, 10 g fiber, 735 mg sodium

Beans are a fabulous weight-loss food. Packed with protein and fiber but virtually no fat, they satisfy your appetite and stave off hunger pangs for hours.

# Chicken and Asparagus Salad with Tarragon Dressing

- ¾ **pound boneless, skinless chicken breast halves**
- 2 **eggs**
- 1 **pound asparagus, tough ends trimmed, cut into 1" pieces**
- ¼ **cup light mayonnaise**
- 2 **teaspoons grated lemon peel**
- ¾ **teaspoon dried tarragon, crumbled**
- ½ **teaspoon stone-ground mustard**
- ½ **teaspoon salt**
- ½ **teaspoon pepper**
- 1 **cucumber, chopped**
- 4 **scallions, thinly sliced**

**PLACE** the chicken in a medium skillet. Add water to just cover. Cover and bring to a boil over high heat. Reduce the heat to low and cook, turning once, for about 10 minutes, or until a thermometer inserted in the thickest portion registers 165°F and the juices run clear. Remove to a plate and let stand until cool enough to handle. Tear into pieces.

**MEANWHILE,** place the eggs in a medium saucepan and cover with cold water. Bring to a boil over high heat. Reduce the heat to low and cook for 10 minutes. Drain and cool under cold running water. Shell and remove the yolks to save for another use. Coarsely chop the whites.

**IN** the same saucepan, bring ½" water to a boil over high heat. Cook the asparagus, stirring often, for about 4 minutes, or until tender-crisp. Drain and cool briefly under cold running water.

**IN** a salad bowl, whisk together the mayonnaise, lemon peel, tarragon, mustard, salt, and pepper. Stir in the cucumber, scallions, chicken, egg whites, and asparagus. Toss gently to mix.

----

Total time: 35 minutes  ✱  Makes 4 servings

Per serving: 220 calories, 24 g protein, 10 g carbohydrates, 9 g total fat, 1 g saturated fat, 3 g fiber, 560 mg sodium

For a different salad, try green beans in place of asparagus, and season with dried savory instead of tarragon.

# Warm Rosemary Beef Salad with Gorgonzola

1 tablespoon chopped fresh rosemary

2 cloves garlic, minced

4 teaspoons extra virgin olive oil, divided

¼ teaspoon salt, divided

¼ teaspoon pepper, divided

1 pound lean top round steak, about ¾" thick

1 head (12 ounces) romaine lettuce, chopped

8 large radishes, quartered

¼ cup crumbled Gorgonzola cheese

2 teaspoons red wine vinegar

**IN** a small bowl, whisk together the rosemary, garlic, 1 teaspoon of the oil, ⅛ teaspoon of the salt, and ⅛ teaspoon of the pepper. Rub evenly on the steak.

**LIGHTLY** coat a grill or grill pan with cooking spray. Preheat to medium-high heat.

**GRILL** the steak for 4 minutes or more per side, depending upon desired degree of doneness, or until a thermometer inserted in the center registers 145°F for medium-rare/160°F for medium/165°F for well-done.

**REMOVE** to a cutting board and let stand for 10 minutes before thinly slicing.

**MEANWHILE,** in a large bowl, combine the lettuce, radishes, cheese, vinegar, and the remaining 3 teaspoons oil, ⅛ teaspoon salt, and ⅛ teaspoon pepper. Divide the salad and steak among 4 plates.

Total time: 25 minutes ✱ Makes 4 servings

Per serving: 250 calories, 29 g protein, 4 g carbohydrates, 12 g total fat, 4 g saturated fat, 2 g fiber, 320 mg sodium

If you're not a fan of Gorgonzola cheese, try fresh goat cheese or feta on this robust main-dish salad.

# Chicken Salad
# with Creamy Honey Dressing

2 tablespoons honey

⅓ cup 0% plain Greek yogurt

¼ teaspoon salt

¼ teaspoon pepper

1½ pounds roasted skinless chicken breast, cut into ½" pieces

¾ cup halved red or green grapes

2 ribs celery, chopped

2 scallions, white part only, sliced

2 tablespoons chopped pistachios

1 head Bibb lettuce

IN a large mixing bowl, whisk together the honey and a small dollop of the yogurt until smooth. Whisk in the remaining yogurt, salt, and pepper. Stir in the chicken, grapes, celery, scallions, and pistachios. Divide the lettuce among 6 plates. Divide the chicken mixture among the leaves.

---

Total time: 10 minutes ✳ Makes 6 servings

Per serving: 250 calories, 38 g protein, 11 g carbohydrates, 5 g total fat, 2 g saturated fat, 1 g fiber, 205 mg sodium

A moderate amount of pistachios boosts the protein while helping to keep saturated fat low.

[ **QUICK TIP: SAVE TIME, EAT HEALTHY**
Take a shortcut to healthy ingredients. Rotisserie chicken? Precut vegetables? Prewashed greens? Bring them on and let them jump-start a good-for-you meal. ]

# Caribbean Seafood and Black Bean Salad

3 tablespoons olive oil

½ pound peeled, deveined medium or large shrimp, cut into chunks

½ pound bay scallops

2 large cloves garlic, minced

1 can (15 ounces) black beans, rinsed and drained

1 cup drained jarred tropical fruit in light syrup

¼ cup chopped fresh cilantro

3 tablespoons frozen lime juice concentrate

1 teaspoon hot-pepper sauce (optional)

½ teaspoon salt

**HEAT** the oil in a medium skillet over medium-high heat. Cook the shrimp, scallops, and garlic, stirring frequently, for 2 minutes, or until the shrimp and scallops are opaque. Remove to a large bowl. Add the beans, fruit, cilantro, lime juice concentrate, hot-pepper sauce (if using), and salt. Stir. Cover and refrigerate for at least 1 hour.

---

Total time: 1 hour 15 minutes ✳ Makes 5 servings

Per serving: 316 calories, 24 g protein, 32 g carbohydrates, 5 g total fat, 1 g saturated fat, 8 g fiber, 406 mg sodium

This tropical dish is also wonderful prepared with catfish in place of the shrimp and scallops.

# Tuna Pasta Salad

4 ounces rigatoni pasta

¼ cup reduced-sodium chicken broth

2 tablespoons lemon juice

2 teaspoons extra virgin olive oil

1 teaspoon dried oregano

1 clove garlic, minced

¼ teaspoon black pepper

1 can (5 ounces) no-salt-added water-packed solid white tuna, drained and flaked

4 ounces frozen and thawed artichoke hearts, patted dry

1 roasted red bell pepper, chopped

4 scallions, white and green parts, thinly sliced

¼ cup crumbled feta cheese

**COOK** the pasta according to package directions. Drain and place in a large bowl.

**MEANWHILE,** in a small bowl, whisk together the broth, lemon juice, oil, oregano, garlic, and black pepper. Pour over the pasta. Stir in the tuna, artichokes, bell pepper, scallions, and cheese.

---

Total time: 15 minutes ✿ Makes 4 servings

Per serving: 212 calories, 13 g protein, 27 g carbohydrates, 6 g total fat, 2 g saturated fat, 3 g fiber, 143 mg sodium

The ever-reliable tuna salad lunch gets a Mediterranean makeover in this pasta mélange, which uses heart-healthy olive oil instead of mayonnaise.

## SUPERFOOD SPOTLIGHT: ARTICHOKES

These versatile green globes (sometimes with a violet tinge) are fun to eat and full of flavor, whether they're full-size or "baby" versions. You'll find artichokes, which supply heart-healthy fiber, folate, and antioxidants, in markets year-round, but their peak season is May. Choose artichokes with tightly closed leaves; avoid any that look dry or brown. Store them in an airtight plastic bag in the refrigerator for up to 5 days.

When fresh artichokes are out of season, turn to frozen loose-pack artichoke hearts.

# Chipotle Crab and Avocado Salad

2  tablespoons reduced-fat mayonnaise

1  tablespoon lemon juice

⅛  teaspoon ground chipotle pepper

Pinch of salt

1  pound lump crabmeat or imitation crabmeat

1  avocado, cut into ¼" cubes

¼  cup fresh basil leaves, loosely torn

¼  roasted red bell pepper, chopped

2  scallions, white and green parts, minced

IN a medium mixing bowl, whisk together the mayonnaise, lemon juice, chipotle pepper, and salt. Stir in the crabmeat, avocado, basil, bell pepper, and scallions.

------

Total time: 10 minutes  ✳  Makes 4 servings

Per serving: 232 calories, 28 g protein, 7 g carbohydrates, 10 g total fat, 1 g saturated fat, 4 g fiber, 560 mg sodium

Chipotle peppers are jalapeño chile peppers that have been dried and smoked. Their deep, intense flavor can be addictive.

## [ WHAT'S IN YOUR . . . IMITATION CRAB? ]

Imitation crab is mostly pollock, a whitefish that delivers low-calorie, low-fat protein while saving you some cholesterol and cash. Even better, the Natural Resources Defense Council puts crab and pollock on its list of seafood containing the least mercury, making it safe to eat once daily. *Caution:* Imitation crab is seasoned with added ingredients, so people with food allergies should read labels carefully.

# Marinated Chickpea Salad

1 can (15 ounces) chickpeas, rinsed and drained

1 small red onion, finely chopped

1 small tomato, chopped

½ green bell pepper, chopped

½ cup chopped reduced-fat provolone cheese

3 tablespoons cider vinegar

2 tablespoons chopped fresh parsley

1 tablespoon extra virgin olive oil

2 large cloves garlic, minced

½ teaspoon dried oregano

¼ teaspoon salt

¼ teaspoon black pepper

IN a large bowl, stir together the chickpeas, onion, tomato, bell pepper, cheese, vinegar, parsley, oil, garlic, oregano, salt, and black pepper. Cover and refrigerate for at least 1 hour.

Total time: 1 hour 10 minutes  ✳  Makes 4 servings

Per serving: 161 calories, 8 g protein, 16 g carbohydrates, 7 g total fat, 2 g saturated fat, 4 g fiber, 475 mg sodium

This salad keeps well in the refrigerator for several days, so it's a convenient lunch or snack when you don't have time to cook. Toss to redistribute the dressing before eating.

# Pear and Smoked Turkey Salad

2 tablespoons rice vinegar or white wine vinegar

4 teaspoons extra virgin olive oil

1 tablespoon honey

2 ounces mixed baby greens

4 Anjou or Bartlett pears, sliced lengthwise

2 ounces thinly sliced smoked turkey breast

2 tablespoons fresh basil leaves, loosely torn

Pinch of pepper

IN a small bowl, whisk together the vinegar, oil, and honey.

DIVIDE the greens, pears, turkey, and basil among 4 plates. Drizzle with the dressing and season to taste with pepper.

---

Total time: 10 minutes  ✳  Makes 4 servings

Per serving: 210 calories, 4 g protein, 40 g carbohydrates, 5 g total fat, 1 g saturated fat, 7 g fiber, 96 mg sodium

Whole grain crispbread is the perfect accompaniment to this salad.

# Warm Lentil Salad with Tomatoes

- 4 cups low-sodium chicken broth
- 2 cups brown lentils
- 1 onion, chopped
- ½ cup balsamic vinegar
- 3 tablespoons honey
- 3 large cloves garlic, minced
- ¼ red bell pepper, chopped
- 1 small tomato, diced
- 2 ribs celery, chopped
- ½ cup chopped fresh parsley
- ¼ cup grated Parmesan cheese
- ¼ teaspoon salt
- ¼ teaspoon black pepper

IN a medium saucepan, bring the broth, lentils, and onion to a boil over medium-high heat. Cook, stirring occasionally, for 20 minutes, or until the lentils are tender but not mushy. Drain and reserve the broth for another use.

IN a large bowl, whisk together the vinegar, honey, and garlic until smooth. Stir in the lentils. Let stand at room temperature, stirring occasionally, for 30 minutes, to allow the lentils to absorb some of the dressing.

STIR in the bell pepper, tomato, celery, parsley, cheese, salt, and black pepper.

---

Total time: 1 hour ✱ Makes 4 servings

Per serving: 360 calories, 22 g protein, 62 g carbohydrates, 3 g total fat, 2 g saturated fat, 20 g fiber, 400 mg sodium

Keep bags of lentils in your pantry. Not only are they nutritious and inexpensive, they don't require presoaking and have the shortest cooking time of any legume.

# Salad with Basil and Walnuts

6 tablespoons extra virgin olive oil

2 tablespoons white wine vinegar

¾ teaspoon salt

1 bag (10 ounces) mixed baby greens

½ cup fresh basil leaves, loosely torn

¼ cup chopped walnuts

IN a large bowl, whisk together the oil, vinegar, and salt. Toss in the greens and basil. Scatter with the nuts.

Total time: 5 minutes   ✱   Makes 4 servings

Per serving: 240 calories, 3 g protein, 3 g carbohydrates, 25 g total fat, 3 g saturated fat, 2 g fiber, 456 mg sodium

With a couple of small slices of leftover roasted chicken breast or pork tenderloin, this quick salad makes a fine lunch.

## NUTRITION NEWS TO USE

People who eat a little more than one serving (about 1¼ cups raw) of leafy greens daily have a 14 percent lower risk of developing type 2 diabetes, according to a recent research review. Raw or cooked, greens like spinach, bok choy, and kale pack a triple whammy: antioxidants, which may reduce inflammation; magnesium, which has been linked to lower diabetes risk; and alpha-linoleic acid, a fatty acid that may cut insulin resistance, say researchers at the University of Leicester in England.

# Creamy Broccoli and Leek Soup

1 small head broccoli (about 1 pound)

1 tablespoon canola oil

1 leek, white part only, sliced

4 cups chicken broth

2 cups evaporated fat-free milk

¼ cup cornstarch

½ teaspoon dried thyme

⅛ teaspoon pepper

**CUT** the broccoli into florets. Peel and discard the tough skin from the stems. Coarsely chop the stems.

**WARM** the oil in a medium saucepan over medium-low heat. Cook the leek, stirring occasionally, for 8 minutes, or until soft. Add the broth and broccoli stems. Bring to a boil, then reduce the heat to low. Cover and cook for 15 minutes, or until the stems are tender but still firm. Add the broccoli florets and simmer for 10 minutes, or until the florets are tender.

**REMOVE** to a food processor or blender. Process for about 2 minutes, or until smooth. Return to the saucepan over medium heat. In a small bowl, whisk together ¼ cup of the milk and the cornstarch until smooth. Slowly stir into the broccoli mixture with the thyme, pepper, and the remaining 1¾ cups milk. Cook and stir for about 3 minutes, or until thickened and bubbly.

Total time: 40 minutes  ✽  Makes 4 servings

Per serving: 254 calories, 20 g protein, 36 g carbohydrates, 4 g total fat, 1 g saturated fat, 5 g fiber, 605 mg sodium

This recipe can be doubled for delicious leftovers. Store in a tightly sealed container in the refrigerator for several days. Reheat in a saucepan or the microwave oven.

# Easy Vegetable Soup

2 potatoes, cubed

¾ cup water

1 tablespoon olive oil

1 onion, chopped

1 rib celery, chopped

2 cloves garlic, minced

2¾ cups reduced-sodium
vegetable broth

1 cup fresh or frozen and
thawed corn kernels

2 ounces green beans, cut into
½" pieces

1 large tomato, chopped

1 teaspoon dried thyme

¾ cup 1% milk

¼ teaspoon salt

¼ teaspoon pepper

**PLACE** the potatoes and water in a small microwaveable bowl. Cover and microwave on high power, stirring halfway through, for 6 minutes. Remove and let stand, covered.

**HEAT** the oil in a large saucepan over medium heat. Cook the onion, celery, and garlic, stirring occasionally, for 5 minutes, or until the onion is soft.

**DRAIN** the potatoes and stir into the saucepan with the broth, corn, green beans, tomato, and thyme. Bring to a boil. Reduce the heat to medium-low, cover, and cook for 10 minutes, or until the beans are tender.

**STIR** in the milk, salt, and pepper. Cook for 5 minutes, or until heated.

---

Total time: 40 minutes ✱ Makes 4 servings

Per serving: 120 calories, 4 g protein, 19 g carbohydrates, 5 g total fat, 1 g saturated fat, 3 g fiber, 280 mg sodium

Taking the time and care to chop vegetables for soup can be a form of meditation. When we prepare food with our own hands, we eat our meals more mindfully.

# Fennel-Cucumber Soup with Shrimp

1 small head fennel with leaves

2 large cucumbers, coarsely chopped

¾ cup ice water

1 cup fat-free sour cream or fat-free plain yogurt

1 tablespoon lemon juice

½ teaspoon salt

¼ teaspoon pepper

¾ pound large shrimp, peeled and deveined

2 teaspoons olive oil

REMOVE the dark lacy leaves from the fennel stalks. Chop and reserve ¼ cup. Trim off and discard the fibrous stalks. Cut the bulb into quarters lengthwise. Remove the core and discard. Cut the remainder into small chunks.

IN a blender or food processor, combine the chopped fennel, cucumbers, and water. Blend for about 45 seconds, or until coarsely pureed. Add the sour cream or yogurt, lemon juice, salt, and pepper. Process, scraping down the bowl as needed, for about 1 minute, or until smooth.

LIGHTLY coat a grill or grill pan with cooking spray. Preheat to medium-high heat. In a small bowl, toss the shrimp with the oil to coat.

GRILL the shrimp for about 1 minute per side, or until opaque.

DIVIDE the soup among 4 bowls. Top with shrimp and fennel leaves.

----

Total time: 15 minutes ✱ Makes 4 servings

Per serving: 190 calories, 22 g protein, 15 g carbohydrates, 5 g total fat, 1 g saturated fat, 2 g fiber, 483 mg sodium

A cup of soup as an appetizer can help you eat less later in the meal. Whip up this refreshing starter when the heat soars.

# Southwest Turkey Soup

1 tablespoon olive oil

2 ounces green beans, finely chopped

1 small onion, chopped

1 jalapeño chile pepper, finely chopped (wear plastic gloves when handling)

2 cloves garlic, minced

1½ teaspoons ground cumin

2½ cups reduced-sodium chicken broth

2½ cups water

1 pound boneless, skinless turkey breast, thinly sliced into 2" strips

1 can (14.5 ounces) Mexican-style diced tomatoes

⅛ teaspoon salt

⅛ teaspoon black pepper

**HEAT** the oil in a large saucepan over medium heat. Cook the beans, onion, jalapeño pepper, garlic, and cumin, stirring occasionally, for 5 minutes, or until the beans are tender-crisp.

**ADD** the broth and water. Increase the heat to high and bring to a rapid simmer. Add the turkey, tomatoes, salt, and black pepper. Reduce the heat to medium. Cook for about 5 minutes, or until the turkey is no longer pink.

---

Total time: 20 minutes　✱　Makes 4 servings

Per serving: 200 calories, 32 g protein, 9 g carbohydrates, 5 g total fat, 1 g saturated fat, 2 g fiber, 541 mg sodium

Add ¼ cup corn kernels for an even more colorful bowl.

---

## HEALTH HEARSAY

**Q: I've heard that all vegetables are the most nutritious when they're raw. Does that mean I should never eat cooked vegetables?**

**A:** Though raw produce is often assumed to be more nutritious than cooked, a mix of both kinds gives you more healthy options. When tomatoes are cooked, they have a higher dose of cancer-fighting lycopene. And cooked zucchini delivers more beta-carotene (a building block for vitamin A) than raw. Cooked spinach is richer in calcium and zinc, while raw spinach has more vitamin C and folate.

# Chicken Soup with Bread Dumplings

1 cup matzoh meal

½ cup seltzer water

1 tablespoon canola oil

4 eggs

½ teaspoon salt

¼ teaspoon pepper

Pinch of ground nutmeg

10 cups reduced-sodium chicken broth

1 carrot, finely chopped

2 tablespoons chopped fresh dill

Prepared horseradish (optional)

IN a medium bowl, stir together the matzoh meal, seltzer, and oil. In a small bowl, whisk together the eggs, salt, pepper, and nutmeg. Stir into the matzoh mixture. Cover and refrigerate for 2 hours.

BRING a large saucepan of water to a boil over high heat.

MEANWHILE, with wet hands, form 16 balls from the dough. Reduce the heat to medium-low, then gently lower the dumplings into the water with a slotted spoon. Cook for about 25 minutes, or until all of the dumplings float to the top and are cooked through.

MEANWHILE, in a large pot, bring the broth and carrot to a simmer over medium-high heat. Cook for 10 minutes, or until the carrot is tender.

DIVIDE the broth, carrot, and dumplings among 8 bowls. Sprinkle with the dill. Serve with horseradish (if using).

Total time: 2 hours 40 minutes  ✳  Makes 8 servings

Per serving: 120 calories, 6 g protein, 15 g carbohydrates, 5 g total fat, 1 g saturated fat, 0 g fiber, 750 mg sodium

Sometimes reaching your goal requires some self-pampering. Simmer up some love-in-a-bowl with this soothing soup.

# Manhattan Clam Chowder

- 2 teaspoons olive oil
- 2 ribs celery with leaves, chopped
- 2 carrots, chopped
- 1 onion, finely chopped
- 1 small clove garlic, minced
- 1 large potato, peeled and chopped
- 2 red or yellow bell peppers, chopped
- 1½ cups water
- 2 cans (6.5 ounces each) chopped clams, drained with juice reserved
- 1 can (14.5 ounces) no-salt-added diced tomatoes
- 1 teaspoon dried thyme
- ¼ teaspoon black pepper
- 3 drops hot-pepper sauce

**HEAT** the oil in a large pot over medium heat. Cook the celery, carrots, onion, and garlic, stirring occasionally, for 5 minutes, or until the onion is tender.

**STIR** in the potato, bell peppers, water, and the reserved clam juice. Bring to a boil. Reduce the heat to low. Cover and cook, stirring occasionally, for 10 minutes, or until the potato is tender.

**STIR** in the tomatoes, thyme, black pepper, hot-pepper sauce, and clams. Cover and simmer for 8 minutes, or until the flavors are blended.

Total time: 40 minutes ✱ Makes 4 servings

Per serving: 180 calories, 10 g protein, 30 g carbohydrates, 3 g total fat, 0 g saturated fat, 5 g fiber, 680 mg sodium



Forget about pasty New England clam chowder. This tomato-based version has more zest, plus it's lower in calories and fat.

# Spinach and Tortellini Soup

3 cups water

1 can (14.5 ounces) reduced-sodium chicken broth

1 package (9 ounces) cheese tortellini

1 package (6 ounces) baby spinach

⅛ teaspoon pepper

4 teaspoons grated Parmesan cheese (optional)

IN a large saucepan, bring the water and broth to a boil over high heat. Reduce the heat to medium. Stir in the pasta. Simmer for about 5 minutes, or until the pasta is tender. Stir in the spinach. Cook for about 1 minute, or until the spinach is just wilted. Season with the pepper and sprinkle with cheese (if using).

Total time: 10 minutes ✱ Makes 4 servings

Per serving: 220 calories, 10 g protein, 35 g carbohydrates, 5 g total fat, 3 g saturated fat, 3 g fiber, 520 mg sodium

With judicious use of packaged ingredients, you can create a soup that tastes homemade in only 10 minutes.

QUICK TIP: BE-LEAF THIS!

100% The amount of your daily requirement for vitamins A and K met in just ½ cup cooked spinach

# Wisconsin Cheese Chowder

1 small red or green bell pepper, finely chopped

1 small onion, finely chopped

3 ribs celery, sliced

¼ cup apple juice

1 clove garlic, minced

⅓ cup all-purpose flour

1 can (14.5 ounces) reduced-sodium chicken broth, divided

4 potatoes, cubed

1 cup fat-free milk

1 cup shredded reduced-fat extra-sharp Cheddar cheese

**IN** a large pot, combine the pepper, onion, celery, apple juice, and garlic. Cook, stirring, over medium-high heat for 5 minutes, or until softened. Stir in the flour to dissolve. Add ½ cup of the broth. Cook and stir for 2 minutes, or until thickened.

**ADD** the potatoes and the remaining broth. Bring to a boil. Reduce the heat to medium. Cover and cook for 20 minutes, or until the potatoes are tender.

**REMOVE** 1 cup of the soup to a blender or food processor. Blend for about 1 minute, or until smooth. Return to the pot. Stir in the milk and cheese. Reduce the heat to low. Cook and stir for 3 minutes, or until the cheese melts.

Total time: 35 minutes  ✱  Makes 4 servings

Per serving: 230 calories, 14 g protein, 36 g carbohydrates, 5 g total fat, 3 g saturated fat, 3 g fiber, 470 mg sodium

Freeze the cooled soup in handy portion-size containers for a lunch to go. To eat, thaw overnight in the refrigerator or in the microwave oven. Cook for 1 to 2 minutes, or until heated through. Stir briskly if the soup separates during reheating.

# Lentil and Escarole Soup

1 onion, chopped

1 small carrot, finely chopped

¼ cup balsamic vinegar

2 cloves garlic, minced

1 teaspoon olive oil

3 cups water

1 can (14.5 ounces) reduced-sodium chicken broth

1 can (14.5 ounces) diced tomatoes

1 cup dried brown lentils

5 ounces escarole, chopped

½ teaspoon pepper

⅛ teaspoon salt

2 tablespoons grated Parmesan cheese

**IN** a large pot over medium-high heat, combine the onion, carrot, vinegar, garlic, and oil. Cook, stirring occasionally, for 5 minutes, or until the carrot softens slightly. Stir in the water, broth, tomatoes, and lentils. Bring almost to a boil. Reduce the heat to medium and cook, stirring occasionally, for 40 minutes, or until the lentils are tender.

**STIR** in the escarole, pepper, and salt. Cook for 5 minutes, or until the escarole wilts. Serve sprinkled with the cheese.

Total time: 55 minutes ✱ Makes 4 servings

Per serving: 240 calories, 16 g protein, 40 g carbohydrates, 3 g total fat, 1 g saturated fat, 17 g fiber, 570 mg sodium

Escarole, a pleasantly bittersweet type of endive, makes this soup distinctive. But if you don't have any on hand, replace it with arugula or baby spinach.

[ **QUICK TIP: SOUP-ER SIZE ME**
20% The reduction in calories eaten in your main course when you have soup first ]

# snacks & little bites

# Baked Filled Wontons

4 ounces Asian stir-fry vegetable mix, finely chopped (1 cup)

2 tablespoons chopped fresh cilantro

1 scallion, green and white parts, minced

1 clove garlic, minced

½ teaspoon grated fresh ginger

½ teaspoon toasted sesame oil

12 wonton skins

¼ cup low-fat cream cheese

Pinch of salt

Pinch of pepper

**PREHEAT** the oven to 350°F. Lightly coat a large nonstick baking sheet with cooking spray.

**IN** a medium bowl, toss together the stir-fry vegetables, cilantro, scallion, garlic, ginger, and oil.

**PLACE** the wonton skins on a work surface. Divide the vegetable mixture and cream cheese among the skins. Dampen the edges and fold over to form a triangle. Press the edges with your fingers to seal. Repeat with the remaining skins.

**PLACE** the wontons on the baking sheet. Sprinkle with the salt and pepper.

**BAKE** for about 12 minutes, or until lightly browned and crisp.

Total time: 25 minutes ✱ Makes 4 servings (3 wontons per serving)

Per serving: 111 calories, 4 g protein, 17 g carbohydrates, 3 g total fat, 1 g saturated fat, 1 g fiber, 208 mg sodium

After assembly, you can keep the filled wontons on the baking sheet, loosely covered, at room temperature for 1 hour before baking.

# Pesto, Tomato, and Provolone Bruschetta

1 French baguette

Olive oil or olive oil cooking spray

¼ cup basil pesto

4 plum tomatoes, cut into 16 lengthwise slices

¼ pound sliced reduced-fat provolone cheese, cut into 16 pieces

**PREHEAT** the oven to 400° F.

**CUT** the baguette into 16 slices. Place on a baking sheet. Bake for about 2 minutes, or until toasted. Remove and lightly coat the toast tops with oil or cooking spray. Divide the pesto, tomatoes, and cheese among the toasts. Bake for about 3 minutes, or until the cheese melts.

Total time: 10 minutes ❋ Makes 8 servings (2 bruschetta per serving)

Per serving: 177 calories, 8 g protein, 21 g carbohydrates, 7 g total fat, 2 g saturated fat, 2 g fiber, 371 mg sodium

Keep slices of French baguette in the freezer so you can enjoy a bruschetta snack whenever the mood strikes. Top with hummus or another healthy spread.

# Chipotle Bean Nachos

1 teaspoon vegetable oil

1 onion, chopped

1 clove garlic, minced

½ pound extra-lean ground beef

1 can (15 ounces) black beans, rinsed and drained

½ can (14.5 ounces) diced tomatoes

2 canned chipotle chile peppers in adobo sauce, chopped, + 1 tablespoon adobo sauce

1 teaspoon ground cumin

1 teaspoon chili powder

¼ teaspoon salt

24 multigrain tortilla chips

¼ cup shredded reduced-fat Cheddar cheese

Sliced pickled jalapeño chile peppers (optional)

Fat-free sour cream (optional)

**PREHEAT** the oven to 450°F.

**HEAT** the oil in a large nonstick skillet over medium heat. Cook the onion and garlic, stirring occasionally, for about 5 minutes, or until tender. Crumble in the beef and cook for about 5 minutes, or until no longer pink. Stir in the beans, tomatoes, chipotle peppers and adobo sauce, cumin, chili powder, and salt. Cook for about 10 minutes, stirring occasionally, or until thickened.

**ARRANGE** the chips on a baking sheet. Divide the bean mixture and cheese among the chips.

**BAKE** for 5 minutes, or until the cheese is melted. Serve topped with pickled jalapeño peppers (if using) and sour cream (if using).

Total time: 35 minutes  ✱  Makes 6 servings (4 chips per serving)

Per serving: 168 calories, 13 g protein, 18 g carbohydrates, 5 g total fat, 1 g saturated fat, 5 g fiber, 555 mg sodium

Now you have more reason than ever to love nachos. These snacks pack a big flavor punch with a low calorie toll.

# Stuffed Cajun Eggs

4 hard-cooked eggs, chilled

¼ cup 1% dry-curd cottage cheese

1 scallion, white and light green parts, minced

¼ teaspoon salt-free Cajun seasoning + extra for garnish

**CUT** the eggs in half lengthwise. Remove the yolks and reserve half of them for another recipe. Place the remaining yolks in a small bowl and mash with a fork. Stir in the cottage cheese, scallion, and seasoning.

**ARRANGE** the egg whites, hollow side up, on a plate. Divide the egg yolk mixture among the hollows. Sprinkle lightly with Cajun seasoning.

Total time: 10 minutes ✻ Makes 8 servings

Per serving: 44 calories, 4 g protein, 1 g carbohydrates, 3 g total fat, 1 g saturated fat, 0 g fiber, 62 mg sodium

Eggs are a terrific source of protein, which helps keep your blood sugar steady. This recipe is superquick if you purchase ready-cooked eggs. Or create your own convenience product by cooking some eggs in advance and refrigerating them in the shells for up to 5 days.

# Greek Chicken Meatballs in Lettuce Cups

1 tablespoon + 2 teaspoons red
  wine vinegar, divided

2 tablespoons extra virgin olive
  oil, divided

  Pinch of red-pepper flakes

1 pound ground chicken breast

2 tablespoons finely crumbled
  feta cheese

2 cloves garlic, minced

1 scallion, white part only,
  minced

12 large leaves Boston lettuce

1 small cucumber, cut into very
  thin strips

½ cup basil leaves, loosely torn

IN a small bowl, combine 1 tablespoon of the vinegar, 1 tablespoon of the oil, and the pepper flakes. Whisk and set aside.

IN a large bowl, combine the chicken, cheese, garlic, scallion, and the remaining 2 teaspoons vinegar and 1 tablespoon oil. With wet hands, form the mixture into 24 meatballs.

LIGHTLY coat a large nonstick skillet with cooking spray. Heat over medium-high heat. Cook the meatballs in 2 batches, turning occasionally, for 5 minutes, or until no longer pink and the juices run clear.

DIVIDE the lettuce among 4 plates. Divide the meatballs among the leaves. Top with the cucumber and basil. Drizzle with the reserved dressing.

Total time: 35 minutes  ✱  Makes 4 servings (6 meatballs per serving)

Per serving: 190 calories, 26 g protein, 3 g carbohydrates, 8 g total fat, 1 g saturated fat, 1 g fiber, 114 mg sodium

[ **METABOLISM BOOSTER: EAT MORE OFTEN** ]
Grazers who divide their eating among six daily mini meals shed more excess pounds than do typical three-meal-a-day eaters, according to William Sears, MD. Same food, same number of calories, but more weight loss.

# Pacific Shrimp Salad

1 tablespoon canola oil

1 pound large shrimp, peeled, deveined, and coarsely chopped

2 ribs celery, finely chopped

⅛ jicama, finely chopped

1 clove garlic, minced

1 teaspoon grated fresh ginger

1 tablespoon reduced-sodium ketchup

1 tablespoon rice wine vinegar

8 large leaves lettuce

1 tablespoon chopped macadamia nuts, toasted (see note page 98)

**HEAT** the oil in a wok or large nonstick skillet over medium-high heat. Cook and stir the shrimp for about 2 minutes, or until opaque. Remove to a small bowl. Set aside.

**ADD** the celery, jicama, garlic, and ginger to the skillet. Cook and stir for 2 minutes, or until tender-crisp. Add the ketchup, vinegar, and the reserved shrimp. Cook for 1 minute, or until heated through.

**DIVIDE** the lettuce among 4 plates. Divide the shrimp mixture among the leaves. Sprinkle with the nuts.

Total time: 10 minutes ✻ Makes 4 servings

Per serving: 156 calories, 21 g protein, 6 g carbohydrates, 5 g total fat, 1 g saturated fat, 2 g fiber, 181 mg sodium

A double serving makes a terrific lunch dish. Scallops or chunks of cooked halibut can replace the shrimp, if you like.

# Asparagus with Smoked Turkey Ribbons

¾ pound asparagus, tough ends trimmed

⅛ pound thinly sliced lower-fat, lower-sodium smoked turkey

2 teaspoons extra virgin olive oil

½ teaspoon lemon juice

½ teaspoon grated lemon peel

Pepper

BRING a large saucepan of lightly salted water to a boil. Cook the asparagus for about 2 minutes, just until tender-crisp. Drain in a colander and immediately run under very cold water for 1 minute to stop the cooking. Drain again and pat dry.

CUT the turkey lengthwise into ½"-wide strips. Wrap around the asparagus spears, beginning right below the tips. Place on a serving platter, drizzle with the oil and lemon juice, and sprinkle with the lemon peel and several pinches of pepper.

-----

Total time: 15 minutes ✱ Makes 6 servings

Per serving: 37 calories, 3 g protein, 3 g carbohydrates, 2 g total fat, 0 g saturated fat, 1 g fiber, 83 mg sodium

As this nosh proves, it doesn't take a lot of work to make your foods look fabulous. Taking time to savor first with your eyes can help slow down your eating.

[ **QUICK TIP: FOR LOWER WEIGHT**
Add chickpeas to salsa. They add bulk and boost your daily intake of protein without adding lots of calories. ]

# Portobello Caps with Pesto and Melted Feta Cheese

1 cup spaghetti sauce

4 large portobello mushroom caps

½ cup finely crumbled reduced-fat feta cheese

1 tablespoon chopped almonds

2 tablespoons basil pesto

1 tablespoon fresh basil leaves, loosely torn (optional)

**PREHEAT** the oven to 375°F. Coat a 9" × 9" baking dish with cooking spray. Spread the sauce in the dish. Arrange the mushroom caps, gill side up, on top. Divide the cheese, nuts, and pesto among the caps.

**BAKE** for 30 minutes, or until browned and bubbly. Sprinkle with the basil (if using).

Total time: 35 minutes  ✱  Makes 4 servings

Per serving: 124 calories, 6 g protein, 11 g carbohydrates, 7 g total fat, 2 g saturated fat, 3 g fiber, 580 mg sodium

Look for jarred spaghetti sauce without added sugar or other sweeteners. Better yet, prepare fresh sauce in bulk and freeze it in recipe-ready portions.

**[ QUICK TIP: A MUSHROOM A DAY**

**64%** The decrease in risk of breast cancer if you eat a white button mushroom daily **]**

# Mushroom Spread

1 ounce porcini or other dried mushrooms

2½ cups boiling water

½ cup brown lentils

1 large onion, finely chopped

8 ounces fresh mushrooms, finely chopped

4 cloves garlic, minced

½ teaspoon dried thyme

¼ cup finely chopped walnuts

¼ teaspoon salt

2 tablespoons chopped fresh parsley

IN a small bowl, combine the porcini and water. Let stand for 15 minutes.

LINE a fine sieve with a coffee filter or paper towels. Set over a medium saucepan. Drain the porcini through the sieve and set aside.

ADD the lentils to the pan. Bring to a boil over high heat. Reduce the heat to medium low. Cover the pan and simmer, stirring occasionally, for 20 minutes, or until all the liquid has been absorbed.

MEANWHILE, coat a medium nonstick skillet with cooking spray. Heat over medium heat. Cook the onion, fresh mushrooms, garlic, thyme, and the reserved porcini, stirring occasionally, for about 15 minutes, or until very soft.

REMOVE the lentils to a food processor. Process for about 2 minutes, scraping the bowl as needed, or until smooth. Add the mushroom mixture, nuts, and salt. Pulse briefly just until combined. Spoon into a serving bowl. Sprinkle with the parsley.

---

Total time: 40 minutes ✽ Makes 8 servings

Per serving: 95 calories, 6 g protein, 12 g carbohydrates, 3 g total fat, 0 g saturated fat, 5 g fiber, 40 mg sodium

This hearty spread keeps well in the refrigerator for up to 3 days. Enjoy it with wheat crackers, crispbread, or raw veggies, or stuff it into Belgian endive leaves or hollowed cherry tomatoes.

## SUPERFOOD SPOTLIGHT: WALNUTS

Walnuts score highest of all nuts in the omega-3s that protect against heart disease. And their stores of fiber and unsaturated fat can help you lower "bad" LDL cholesterol naturally. To preserve taste and prevent spoiling, keep shelled nuts refrigerated in an airtight container for up to 6 months or in the freezer for up to a year.

# Greek Yogurt Veggie Spread

¼ cup apple juice

½ small onion, finely chopped

½ small carrot, finely chopped

1 teaspoon chopped fresh or dried chives

2 cups 0% plain Greek yogurt
  Paprika

12 thin rye crackers

IN a small skillet, bring the apple juice to a boil over medium-high heat. Cook the onion, carrot, and chives, stirring occasionally, for about 5 minutes, or until the vegetables are soft.

PLACE the yogurt in a mixing bowl. Stirring slowly, gradually add the vegetable mixture. Spoon into a serving bowl. Cover and refrigerate for 1 hour.

DUST with paprika and serve with the crackers.

---

Total time: 1 hour 10 minutes  ✽  Makes 6 servings (2 crackers per serving)

Per serving: 63 calories, 7 g protein, 8 g carbohydrates, 0 g total fat, 0 g saturated fat, 1 g fiber, 42 mg sodium

This speedy spread provides a blueprint for many variations. Try different flavoring combinations with finely chopped bell pepper, zucchini, or green beans.

[ **LABEL DECODER: SPOT HIDDEN SUGAR**
Avoid products with any form of sugar in the first five ingredients. If the word is a "syrup" or ends in -ose, it's an added sweetener. ]

# Crudités with Spicy Peanut Dipping Sauce

⅓ cup natural peanut butter

2 small hot chile peppers, seeded and chopped (wear plastic gloves when handling)

¼ cup lime juice

3 tablespoons mango nectar or apple cider

2 tablespoons soy sauce

1 large clove garlic, halved

¼ teaspoon salt

½ pound assorted raw vegetables

IN a blender or food processor, combine the peanut butter, chile peppers, lime juice, nectar or cider, soy sauce, garlic, and salt. Blend or process for about 2 minutes, adding a teaspoon or two of water as needed, or until a smooth sauce forms. Serve with the vegetables.

------

Total time: 5 minutes  ✱  Makes 8 servings

Per serving: 85 calories, 3 g protein, 6 g carbohydrates, 5 g total fat, 1 g saturated fat, 3 g fiber, 381 mg sodium

Broccoli florets, cauliflower florets, baby carrots, zucchini sticks, and thin asparagus spears all make crispy dippers for this rich sauce.

# Spinach-Arugula Dip

1 cup 1% dry-curd cottage cheese

½ cup packed baby spinach

¼ cup packed arugula leaves

2 tablespoons (½ ounce) grated Romano cheese

½ teaspoon salt-free lemon-pepper seasoning

**IN** a food processor, combine the cottage cheese, spinach, arugula, Romano cheese, and seasoning blend. Pulse about 12 times, or until the greens are chopped.

Total time: 5 minutes  ✳  Makes 5 servings

Per serving: 49 calories, 7 g protein, 2 g carbohydrates, 1 g total fat, 1 g saturated fat, 0 g fiber, 236 mg sodium

Accompany this easy appetizer with raw vegetables or whole grain crackers. It can also double as a delicious sandwich spread on whole grain toast. It keeps well in an airtight container in the refrigerator for up to 3 days.

# Pesto Crostini

½ loaf Italian bread

2 cloves garlic, halved

2 tablespoons basil pesto

2 tablespoons grated Parmesan cheese

**PREHEAT** the oven to 350°F.

**CUT** the bread into 12 thin slices. Place on a baking sheet. Rub the garlic on top of the slices. Divide the pesto and cheese, spreading evenly, among the slices.

**BAKE** for 10 minutes, or until lightly browned.

Total time: 15 minutes ✱ Makes 4 servings (3 crostini per serving)

Per serving: 240 calories, 9 g protein, 35 g carbohydrates, 7 g total fat, 3 g saturated fat, 2 g fiber, 586 mg sodium

For more pungent toasts, try using half Romano cheese. Sliced cherry tomatoes make a pretty topping.

# Paprika Corn Wafers

⅔ cup yellow cornmeal

½ teaspoon salt

⅛ teaspoon chili powder

1¼ cups water

2 tablespoons trans-free spread or butter, cut into small pieces

Paprika for dusting

**PREHEAT** the oven to 400°F. Line 2 large baking sheets with foil. Coat generously with cooking spray.

**IN** a medium bowl, stir together the cornmeal, salt, and chili powder.

**IN** a microwaveable bowl, combine the water and spread or butter. Microwave on high power for about 90 seconds, or until the water boils. Stir into the cornmeal mixture. Let stand for 5 minutes. The batter will be very thin.

**STIRRING** after each spoonful, drop the batter by teaspoonfuls onto 1 baking sheet. Spoon only 3 to a row and no more than 8 on a sheet because they spread.

**BAKE** for about 8 minutes, or until dry and very lightly browned at the edges. Lift off carefully with a wide spatula and remove to a rack to cool.

**REPEAT** with the remaining batter, coating the foil with cooking spray before each batch.

**DUST** with paprika.

-----

Total time: 45 minutes ✳ Makes 24 servings

Per serving: 19 calories, 0 g protein, 3 g carbohydrates, 1 g total fat, 0 g saturated fat, 0 g fiber, 34 mg sodium

Making your own crackers is a fun family activity and guarantees no unwanted additives, colorings, or artificial ingredients.

# Zucchini Chips

2 large zucchini (12 ounces each)

1 tablespoon olive oil

¼ teaspoon salt

¼ teaspoon garlic powder

**PREHEAT** the oven to 400°F. Coat 2 baking sheets with cooking spray.

**CUT** the zucchini diagonally into ⅛"-thick slices. Place in a large bowl and toss well with the oil, salt, and garlic powder. Spread out on the baking sheets.

**BAKE,** turning often, for 25 minutes. Reduce the oven temperature to 300°F and bake for about 15 minutes, or until speckled brown and crisp. Remove to paper towels and let cool.

Total time: 50 minutes ✽ Makes 4 servings

Per serving: 56 calories, 2 g protein, 6 g carbohydrates, 4 g total fat, 1 g saturated fat, 2 g fiber, 162 mg sodium

Surprise your guests with a smarter party snack! These crispy veggie munchies will keep at room temperature, uncovered, for several hours.

## QUICK TIP: STOP 3:00 P.M. SLUMPS

If an oversize handful of M&M's is your usual antidote to a postlunch energy free fall, try this quick fatigue fighter at your desk from Mao Shing Ni, PhD, a 38th-generation doctor of Chinese medicine: Indulge in an orange. The pick-me-up scent of citrus can increase your energy, research shows. Stimulating the olfactory nerve inside your nose activates the limbic system of your brain, which is associated with mood and triggered by citrus.

# Banana Snack Cake

2 teaspoons + 1 cup whole grain pastry flour

½ teaspoon baking soda

½ teaspoon baking powder

Pinch of salt

2 egg whites

1 egg, separated

8 tablespoons granulated sugar, divided

¼ cup canola oil

½ cup mashed very ripe banana

¼ cup buttermilk

2 teaspoons confectioners' sugar

2 teaspoons unsweetened cocoa powder

PREHEAT the oven to 350°F. Coat an 8" × 8" baking pan with cooking spray. Dust with 2 teaspoons flour, shaking off excess. Set aside.

IN a large bowl, stir together the remaining 1 cup flour, the baking soda, baking powder, and salt. Set aside.

IN a mixing bowl, beat the 3 egg whites with an electric mixer on high speed for about 2 minutes, or until foamy. Continue beating, while adding 2 tablespoons of the granulated sugar, for about 1 minute, or until stiff peaks form.

IN a mixing bowl, with an electric mixer and the same beaters, beat the oil and the remaining 6 tablespoons sugar until smooth. One at a time, beat in the egg yolk, banana, and buttermilk, until blended. On low speed, gradually add the reserved dry ingredients, mixing until blended. Stir a large spoonful of the egg whites into the batter. Fold in the remaining whites. Pour into the baking pan.

BAKE for about 30 minutes, or until golden and the cake starts to come away from the sides of the pan. Cool in the pan on a rack for 5 minutes. Turn the cake onto the rack and cool completely.

IN a small bowl, stir together the confectioners' sugar and cocoa powder. Sift through a fine sieve over the cake.

------

Total time: 45 minutes ✳ Makes 9 servings

Per serving: 164 calories, 3 g protein, 23 g carbohydrates, 7 g total fat, 1 g saturated fat, 2 g fiber, 136 mg sodium

Sure to become a family favorite, this easy cake makes perfect use of an overripe banana. By using egg whites and buttermilk, we've kept the fat low but retained the moist goodness.

# Strawberry Energizer Bars

2 cups low-fat granola, coarsely chopped

¾ cup roasted unsalted cashews, coarsely chopped

¾ cup dried strawberries, coarsely chopped

2 tablespoons whole grain flour

½ cup sesame seeds

⅓ cup honey or packed light brown sugar

½ teaspoon salt

2 egg whites

½ teaspoon vanilla extract

PREHEAT the oven to 300°F. Line a 9" × 9" baking pan with foil. Coat with cooking spray.

IN a large bowl, stir together the granola, nuts, strawberries, flour, and sesame seeds.

IN a small bowl, whisk together the honey or sugar and salt. Whisk in the egg whites and vanilla. Stir into the dry ingredients. With moistened hands or plastic wrap, pat the mixture into the baking pan.

BAKE for about 50 minutes, or until dry to the touch. Cool in the pan on a rack.

WITH a knife or kitchen shears dipped in hot water, cut into 18 bars. Wrap each bar in waxed paper and store in an airtight tin for up to 2 weeks.

Total time: 1 hour 30 minutes  ✱  Makes 18

Per bar: 128 calories, 3 g protein, 18 g carbohydrates, 5 g total fat, 1 g saturated fat, 1 g fiber, 104 mg sodium

Some packaged energy bars contain so much added sweetener that they may as well be candy bars. We've created an easy-to-make, nutritious alternative with plenty of fiber and nutrients.

## QUICK TIP: APPLES AID DIGESTION

18% The daily requirement for fiber found in one medium apple

# Peanut Butter and Raisin Porcupines

½ cup all-bran cereal with extra fiber

¼ cup raisins

2 tablespoons nonfat dry milk

¼ cup + 1 tablespoon part-skim ricotta cheese

3 tablespoons natural peanut butter

PLACE the cereal in a shallow dish. With your hands, crumble into smaller pieces.

IN a food processor, combine the raisins and dry milk. Process for about 2 minutes, or until the raisins are finely chopped. Remove to a small bowl. Stir in the ricotta and peanut butter until smooth.

LIGHTLY coat your hands with cooking spray. One at a time, shape the raisin mixture into small balls (2 level teaspoons each). Roll each ball into the cereal to coat lightly. Press to adhere. Set the balls in a plastic storage container. If there is more than 1 layer, separate with a sheet of waxed paper.

---

Total time: 15 minutes ✳ Makes 7 servings (5 porcupines per serving)

Per serving: 88 calories, 4 g protein, 10 g carbohydrates, 5 g total fat, 1 g saturated fat, 3 g fiber, 70 mg sodium

These satisfying morsels keep well in an airtight container in the refrigerator for up to 1 week, so have them on hand to stave off junk-food cravings.

[ **QUICK TIP: SPREAD IT AROUND**
Getting bored with peanut butter? Try sweet almond butter instead. Ounce for ounce, almond butter provides 88 percent more bone-building calcium than peanut butter does. ]

# Dried Fruit Truffles

½ cup pitted prunes

½ cup pitted dates

½ cup dried apricots

1 tablespoon grated fresh lemon peel or dried

½ cup granulated sugar

2 tablespoons trans-free spread or butter

1 tablespoon honey

2 tablespoons frozen orange juice concentrate, thawed

1 teaspoon ground cinnamon

1½ cups crispy rice cereal

2 tablespoons confectioners' sugar

IN a food processor, combine the prunes, dates, apricots, and lemon peel. Process for about 2 minutes, or until finely chopped. Set aside.

IN a heavy saucepan over medium-low heat, combine the sugar, spread or butter, honey, orange juice concentrate, and cinnamon. Cook, stirring occasionally, for about 5 minutes, or until the sugar is dissolved. Add the cereal and reserved fruit mixture. Stir to coat well. Remove from the heat and set aside to cool.

COAT your palms with cooking spray. Pinch off small pieces of the mixture and roll into 1" balls. Place the confectioners' sugar in a shallow bowl or pie pan. Roll the balls in the sugar and set on waxed paper to dry. Store in an airtight tin for up to 1 week.

----

Total time: 40 minutes  ✳  Makes 12 servings (3 truffles per serving)

Per serving: 123 calories, 1 g protein, 28 g carbohydrates, 2 g total fat, 1 g saturated fat, 2 g fiber, 34 mg sodium

For a naughty variation, replace ½ cup crispy rice cereal with mini chocolate chips. Shhh! It's our secret.

# Banana–Brown Sugar Cookies

1¼ cups whole grain pastry flour

¾ cup old-fashioned rolled oats

¼ cup wheat bran

½ teaspoon baking soda

½ teaspoon ground cinnamon

¼ teaspoon salt

½ cup dark raisins

1 cup mashed very ripe banana

⅓ cup packed light brown sugar

3 tablespoons canola oil

1 egg

1 teaspoon vanilla extract

**PREHEAT** the oven to 350°F. Coat 2 baking sheets with cooking spray.

**IN** a large bowl, combine the flour, oats, bran, baking soda, cinnamon, and salt. Stir in the raisins. In a medium bowl, whisk together the bananas, sugar, oil, egg, and vanilla. Stir into the dry ingredients just until blended. Drop the batter in 24 level tablespoonfuls onto the baking sheets. Flatten the tops slightly with a rubber spatula.

**BAKE** for about 12 minutes, or until the cookies are lightly browned. Cool on the pans on a rack for 5 minutes. Remove to the rack and cool completely.

------------------------------------------------

Total time: 30 minutes ✱ Makes 24

Per cookie: 84 calories, 2 g protein, 15 g carbohydrates, 2 g total fat, 0 g saturated fat, 2 g fiber, 55 mg sodium

Who wouldn't love an old-fashioned chewy drop cookie with only 84 calories?

# Citrus Cookies

1¼ cups all-purpose flour

3 tablespoons Splenda or granulated sugar substitute

4 tablespoons confectioners' sugar, divided

1 teaspoon lemon extract

1 teaspoon orange extract

1 teaspoon baking powder

¼ cup trans-free spread or butter

1 egg

1 tablespoon orange juice or lemon juice

**IN** a food processor, combine the flour, Splenda or sugar substitute, 3 tablespoons of the confectioners' sugar, the lemon extract, orange extract, and baking powder. Add the spread or butter and pulse on and off until coarse crumbs form. Add the egg and juice and process just until a dough forms. Shape into a ball and cover with plastic wrap. Refrigerate for at least 1 hour, or until firm.

**PREHEAT** the oven to 350°F. Coat a baking sheet with cooking spray.

**SHAPE** the dough into 1" balls and place them 1" apart on the baking sheet.

**BAKE** for 10 minutes, or until golden. Cool on the pan on a rack for 5 minutes. Remove to the rack and cool completely. Dust with the remaining 1 tablespoon confectioners' sugar.

-----

Total time: 1 hour 10 minutes ✱ Makes 24 cookies

Per cookie: 52 calories, 1 g protein, 8 g carbohydrates, 2 g total fat, 1 g saturated fat, 0 g fiber, 36 mg sodium

Keep these zesty gems in the freezer. When you crave a treat that won't damage your waistline, take out 2 and thaw at room temperature for 10 minutes.

# Apricot-Honey Spice Bars

1 cup whole grain pastry flour

¼ teaspoon baking powder

¼ teaspoon baking soda

½ teaspoon ground cinnamon

¼ teaspoon salt

¾ cup coarsely chopped dried apricots

¼ cup golden raisins

1 egg

1 egg white

¼ cup + 1 tablespoon honey

¼ cup canola oil

¼ cup brewed tea, cooled

**PREHEAT** the oven to 350°F. Coat an 8" × 8" baking pan with cooking spray.

**IN** a large bowl, stir together the flour, baking powder, baking soda, cinnamon, and salt until blended. Stir in the apricots and raisins.

**IN** a medium bowl, whisk together the egg, egg white, ¼ cup of the honey, the oil, and tea. Stir into the dry ingredients until no flour is visible. Pour into the baking pan.

**BAKE** for about 20 minutes, or until golden brown and a wooden pick inserted in the center comes out clean. Cool in the pan on a rack for 30 minutes.

**BRUSH** with the remaining 1 tablespoon honey. Let stand for about 1 hour to cool completely. Cut into 12 bars.

Total time: 2 hours  ✻  Makes 12

Per bar: 116 calories, 2 g protein, 16 g carbohydrates, 5 g total fat, 1 g saturated fat, 1 g fiber, 111 mg sodium

The fiber and nutrients in apricots and other dried fruits make them oh-so-good candidates for healthy snacks.

# Crunchy Peanut Butter Cookies

1¾ cups all-purpose flour

¾ teaspoon baking soda

¼ teaspoon salt

¾ cup packed light brown sugar

¼ cup granulated sugar

5 tablespoons trans-free spread or butter

¼ cup no-salt-added crunchy peanut butter

3 tablespoons water

1 egg white

1 teaspoon vanilla extract

**PREHEAT** the oven to 350°F. Coat 2 nonstick baking sheets with cooking spray.

**IN** a medium bowl, stir together the flour, baking soda, and salt.

**IN** a mixing bowl, beat together the brown sugar, granulated sugar, spread or butter, and peanut butter until smooth. Beat in the water, egg white, and vanilla until light. Stir in the dry ingredients just until no flour is visible.

**SHAPE** the dough into 1" balls and place on the baking sheets, leaving 2" between cookies. Dip a fork in water and flatten the cookies with a crisscross pattern.

**BAKE** for about 10 minutes, or until the cookies are just set. Cool on the pans on a rack for 2 minutes. Remove to the rack and cool completely.

--------------------------------------------

Total time: 45 minutes  ✱  Makes 30

Per cookie: 85 calories, 1 g protein, 13 g carbohydrates, 3 g total fat, 1 g saturated fat, 0 g fiber, 65 mg sodium

We slimmed down this much-loved cookie by using less peanut butter and just 1 egg white in place of eggs.

# Trail Mix

2 cups oat circle cereal

1 cup dried pineapple, chopped

1 cup dried blueberries

1 cup dried apricots, sliced

¼ cup dried strawberries

⅓ cup unsalted dry-roasted peanuts

¼ cup semisweet chocolate chips

¼ cup dry-roasted sunflower seeds

IN a mixing bowl, stir together the cereal, pineapple, blueberries, apricots, strawberries, peanuts, chips, and sunflower seeds. Store in an airtight container for up to 1 week.

----

Total time: 10 minutes ✳ Makes 12 servings (½ cup each)

Per serving: 199 calories, 3 g protein, 37 g carbohydrates, 5 g total fat, 1 g saturated fat, 4 g fiber, 47 mg sodium

When you keep bags of this good-for-you snack in your desk, your car, and your handbag, you can kiss the vending machine good-bye.

## HEALTH HEARSAY

Q: Is it true that you have to grind up flaxseed to get the omega-3s?

A: Yes. It's easier to digest ground flaxseed, which means you absorb more of the nutritional benefits—including omega-3s. The whole seeds may pass through your system undigested. Get maximum nutritional benefits by using a coffee grinder to grind up the seeds as you need them (whole seeds can last several months in the fridge). Try sprinkling ground flaxseed on yogurt, salads, and soups. If you're purchasing already ground flaxseed, look for brands packaged in opaque bags that help retain nutrients.

# Oat-Nut Brittle

1 cup quick-cooking oats

½ cup fiber cereal

½ cup slivered almonds

¼ cup salted oil-roasted peanuts

1 cup sugar

¼ cup maple syrup

2 tablespoons lemon juice

1 teaspoon grated lemon peel

¼ teaspoon salt

2 tablespoons trans-free spread or butter

PREHEAT the oven to 350°F.

ON a baking sheet, stir together the oats, cereal, almonds, and peanuts. Bake, stirring occasionally, for about 12 minutes, or until the oats are lightly toasted. Remove to a medium bowl. Coat the baking sheet with cooking spray.

IN a heavy saucepan over medium-high heat, stir together the sugar, syrup, lemon juice, lemon peel, and salt. Bring to a boil and cook, stirring occasionally, for about 8 minutes, or until the sugar has dissolved and turned golden (325°F on a candy thermometer). Remove from the heat and stir in the spread or butter until melted. Pour over the oat mixture, stirring to coat well. Pour onto the baking sheet and top with a piece of parchment paper. With a rolling pin, roll into a thin sheet. Peel off the paper and let cool for 45 minutes. Break into pieces.

Total time: 1 hour 15 minutes  ✱  Makes 12 servings

Per serving: 177 calories, 3 g protein, 30 g carbohydrates, 6 g total fat, 2 g saturated fat, 3 g fiber, 83 mg sodium

This crunchy confection is chock-full of grains and nuts made yummy with maple syrup and lemon.

# Seeded Almond Mix

4 cups unblanched almonds

1 cup sunflower seeds

½ cup sesame seeds

2 tablespoons soy sauce

1 teaspoon toasted sesame oil

PREHEAT the oven to 350°F. Coat a rimmed baking sheet with cooking spray.

IN a large bowl, stir together the almonds, sunflower seeds, sesame seeds, soy sauce, and oil. Spread out on the baking sheet.

BAKE, stirring occasionally, for about 12 minutes, or until crisp. Cool on the pan on a rack. Store in an airtight container.

Total time: 15 minutes ✱ Makes 22 servings (¼ cup per serving)

Per serving: 209 calories, 8 g protein, 8 g carbohydrates, 18 g total fat, 2 g saturated fat, 4 g fiber, 93 mg sodium

An exotic touch of soy and sesame takes these nuts and seeds from bland to bewitching.

# Oatmeal-Granola Marshmallow Treats

2 tablespoons trans-free spread
or butter

30 marshmallows

3 cups oat circle cereal

3 cups mixed fruit granola

**COAT** an 8" × 8" baking dish with cooking spray.

**MELT** the spread or butter in a large saucepan over medium heat. Cook the marshmallows, stirring occasionally, for about 6 minutes, or until melted. Remove from the heat and stir in the cereal and granola until well coated. Pour into the baking dish. Place a piece of waxed paper over the mixture and press down firmly with the palm of your hand to flatten. Let cool in the pan on a rack for 30 minutes.

**REMOVE** from the pan and set on a cutting board for 30 minutes, or until completely cooled. Cut into 16 pieces. Store in an airtight container up to 5 days.

------------------------------------------------------

Total time: 1 hour 10 minutes ✱ Makes 16

Per treat: 163 calories, 3 g protein, 31 g carbohydrates, 4 g total fat, 1 g saturated fat, 2 g fiber, 71 mg sodium

This more nutritious version of marshmallow treats proves that a spoonful of sugar *does* help the medicine go down.

[ **QUICK TIP: GET WHOLE**
46% The decrease in heart disease risk for people who eat the most whole grains ]

# Kiwifruit Shake

½ quart fat-free vanilla frozen
   yogurt

1 very ripe kiwifruit, sliced

IN a blender, combine the yogurt and kiwifruit. Blend for about 2 minutes, scraping the sides of the bowl as needed, or until smooth.

------

Total time: 5 minutes ✱ Makes 2 servings

Per serving: 214 calories, 10 g protein, 44 g carbohydrates, 1 g total fat, 0 g saturated fat, 1 g fiber, 130 mg sodium

If kiwifruit are firm when you buy them, ripen at room temperature for a few days in a fruit bowl or brown paper bag with some bananas.

# Chocolate Malted Milkshake

¾  cup fat-free vanilla frozen yogurt

3  tablespoons malted milk powder

1½  tablespoons unsweetened cocoa powder

½  teaspoon instant espresso powder

1  cup soy milk or 1% milk

1  teaspoon vanilla extract

IN a blender, combine the yogurt, malted milk powder, cocoa, espresso powder, milk, and vanilla. Blend for about 1 minute, or until smooth.

Total time: 5 minutes  ✳  Makes 2 servings

Per serving: 230 calories, 12 g protein, 41 g carbohydrates, 3 g total fat, 1 g saturated fat, 3 g fiber, 171 mg sodium

Think you have to suffer to achieve your ideal weight? Not with snacks like this frosty protein-packed treat.

## QUICK TIP: DRINK YOURSELF THIN

15.5 The number of pounds that dieters lost over 3 months when they drank 2 cups of water before meals, a 44 percent increase in weight loss compared with those who didn't. Kicking off a meal with water shrinks your appetite, so you consume fewer calories, say researchers at Virginia Tech University.

# Iced Orange-Coconut Drink

1 cup orange juice

½ cup unsweetened soy milk

½ cup unsweetened shredded coconut

Ice

**IN** a blender, combine the orange juice, milk, and coconut. Blend for about 2 minutes, or until smooth. Serve over ice.

Total time: 5 minutes ✱ Makes 2 servings

Per serving: 200 calories, 4 g protein, 19 g carbohydrates, 13 g total fat, 11 g saturated fat, 4 g fiber, 16 mg sodium

Store extra servings in a jar in the refrigerator for up to 12 hours. Shake before drinking.

# Pineapple Slushie

¾ cup canned crushed
  pineapple

1 cup crushed ice

¼ cup lemon sorbet

¼ cup ice water

**IN** a blender, combine the pineapple, ice, sorbet, and water. Blend for about 2 minutes, or until a slushy consistency.

--------------------------------------------------

Total time: 5 minutes ✱ Makes 1 serving

Per serving: 104 calories, 1 g protein, 26 g carbohydrates, 0 g total fat, 0 g saturated fat, 1 g fiber, 21 mg sodium

For a balanced snack, enjoy this refreshing beverage while munching on 2 tablespoons almonds.

[ **QUICK TIP: SWEET C**

37% Amount of the daily recommendation for vitamin C in 1 cup of pineapple ]

# dinners

# Beef Burgundy

2 tablespoons all-purpose flour

3¼ cups reduced-sodium chicken broth, divided

8 ounces fresh mushrooms, sliced

1 onion, chopped

½ cup dry red wine (optional)

1 pound lean beef chuck roast, trimmed of all visible fat and cut into 2" cubes

1 tablespoon tomato paste

2 cloves garlic, minced

¾ teaspoon pepper

½ teaspoon salt

¼ teaspoon dried thyme

**IN** a mixing bowl, whisk together the flour and ¼ cup of the broth.

**COAT** a large pot with cooking spray. Heat over medium-high heat. Cook the mushrooms, onion, ½ cup of the broth, and the wine (if using), stirring occasionally, for 8 minutes, or until the liquid has almost evaporated. Remove to a plate.

**ADD** the beef and ½ cup of the broth to the pot. Cook, stirring occasionally, for 5 minutes, or until the beef is no longer pink. Stir in the tomato paste, garlic, pepper, salt, thyme, and the remaining 2 cups broth. Bring to a boil. Reduce the heat to medium-low. Add the mushroom-onion mixture. Cover and cook for 30 minutes, or until the beef is fork-tender.

**WITH** a slotted spoon, remove the beef and vegetables to a serving bowl. Cover to keep warm. Whisk about 1 cup of the sauce into the bowl with the flour and broth. Increase the heat to high. Whisk, gradually adding the flour mixture, for about 2 minutes, or until thickened. Return the beef and vegetables to the pot. Simmer for 1 minute, or until heated through.

--------

Total time: 55 minutes ✱ Makes 4 servings

Per serving: 206 calories, 28 g protein, 9 g carbohydrates, 6 g total fat, 2 g saturated fat, 1 g fiber, 749 mg sodium

Like most stews, this hearty dish tastes even more delicious when it's reheated. Prepare it several days ahead for a no-work weeknight supper.

# Chinese Beef and Pasta Skillet Supper

1 pound lean beef chuck roast, trimmed of all visible fat and cut into 2" cubes

1 cup unsweetened pineapple juice

1 tablespoon reduced-sodium soy sauce

1 tablespoon packed light brown sugar

1½ teaspoons toasted sesame oil

2 carrots, sliced

1 onion, chopped

1 clove garlic, minced

½ teaspoon grated fresh ginger

4 ounces whole grain spaghetti

1 bunch scallions, white and light green parts, thinly sliced

IN a large resealable plastic bag, combine the beef, pineapple juice, soy sauce, and sugar. Seal and massage to mix well. Refrigerate, massaging occasionally, for 1 hour.

COAT a large nonstick skillet with cooking spray. Heat the oil over medium-high heat. Cook and stir the carrots, onion, garlic, and ginger for 5 minutes, or until the onion is soft but not browned. Add the beef and marinade. Cook, stirring occasionally, for 10 minutes, or until the beef is no longer pink. Check by inserting the tip of a sharp knife into 1 cube.

COOK the spaghetti for 2 minutes less time than package directions. Drain and add to the pan along with the scallions. Toss well. Reduce the heat to low. Cover and cook for 2 minutes, or until the spaghetti has absorbed some of the sauce.

---

Total time: 1 hour 30 minutes ✳ Makes 4 servings

Per serving: 346 calories, 31 g protein, 39 g carbohydrates, 8 g total fat, 3 g saturated fat, 5 g fiber, 247 mg sodium

Kick the Chinese carryout habit with this terrific beef and pasta skillet supper.

## GOTTA TRY IT: THE SKINNY ON CAST-IRON SKILLETS

A simple cast-iron skillet—like the one your grandmother used—still ranks as one of the best cooking utensils ever made. It gives you a nearly nonstick surface, without the possibly harmful fumes generated by preheating chemically treated nonstick pans. It browns food beautifully, evenly, and easily. Plus, you can use it on top of the stove or in the oven. Look for a heavy pan to ensure even heat distribution. Preseasoned skillets dominate the market right now. They're ready to go without the messy business of seasoning—greasing and baking for at least an hour and then repeating the process—before you start using the pan for cooking.

# Fettuccine and Meatballs

½ pound extra-lean ground beef

6 tablespoons grated Romano cheese, divided

¼ cup whole wheat bread crumbs

1 egg

1 teaspoon dried oregano, divided

¾ teaspoon pepper, divided

2 teaspoons olive oil

1 onion, finely chopped

2 cloves garlic, minced

2 zucchini, halved lengthwise and sliced

1 yellow squash, halved lengthwise and sliced

1 can (28 ounces) crushed tomatoes

8 ounces whole grain fettuccine

IN a large bowl, stir together the beef, 4 tablespoons of the cheese, the bread crumbs, egg, ½ teaspoon of the oregano, and ½ teaspoon of the pepper. Form into walnut-size balls.

COAT a large nonstick skillet with cooking spray. Heat over medium heat. Working in batches, cook the meatballs, turning as needed, for 15 minutes, or until no longer pink. Remove to a platter, leaving drippings in the skillet.

ADD the oil to the skillet over medium-high heat. Cook and stir the onion and garlic for 2 minutes, or until the onion is translucent. Stir in the zucchini and yellow squash. Cook, stirring occasionally, for about 5 minutes, or until the zucchini and squash are lightly browned. Stir in the tomatoes; the remaining ½ teaspoon oregano and ¼ teaspoon pepper; and the meatballs. Bring almost to a boil and then reduce the heat to low. Cover and cook for 20 minutes to allow the flavors to blend.

MEANWHILE, cook the pasta according to package directions. Drain and divide among 4 plates. Top with the sauce and meatballs. Garnish with the remaining 2 tablespoons cheese.

----

Total time: 1 hour ✱ Makes 6 servings

Per serving: 461 calories, 31 g protein, 58 g carbohydrates, 10 g total fat, 4 g saturated fat, 12 g fiber, 571 mg sodium

Don't abandon your beloved dinnertime favorites while you're slimming down. Just make them healthier, like this delectable pasta-with-meatballs classic.

# Beef and Black Bean Picadillo with Rice

1 cup instant brown rice

¾ pound extra-lean ground beef

2 teaspoons olive oil

1 red bell pepper, coarsely chopped

1 red onion, chopped

2 cloves garlic, minced

2½ teaspoons ground cumin

½ teaspoon red-pepper flakes

¼ teaspoon salt

1 can (15–16 ounces) black beans, rinsed and drained

1 can (14.5 ounces) no-salt-added diced tomatoes in juice

½ cup dark raisins

2 tablespoons pimiento-stuffed olives

**COOK** the rice according to package directions.

**COAT** a large nonstick skillet with cooking spray. Heat over medium-high heat. Crumble in the beef and cook, stirring to break up any chunks, for about 5 minutes, or until no longer pink. Drain and set aside.

**ADD** the oil to the skillet and heat over medium heat. Cook and stir the bell pepper, onion, and garlic for about 5 minutes, or until softened. Return the beef to the pan and stir in the cumin, pepper flakes, and salt. Cook and stir for 1 minute. Stir in the beans, tomatoes, and raisins. Bring to a simmer. Reduce the heat to low.

**COVER** and cook, stirring occasionally, for 15 minutes, or until the flavors have blended.

**SPRINKLE** with the olives. Serve with the rice.

---

Total time: 35 minutes ✲ Makes 4 servings

Per serving: 431 calories, 29 g protein, 60 g carbohydrates, 9 g total fat, 2 g saturated fat, 11 g fiber, 214 mg sodium

Black beans are easy on the tummy, causing very little digestive upset. Plus they're versatile and full of fiber and protein.

# Tuscan-Style Stuffed Peppers

½ cup instant brown rice

¾ pound extra-lean ground beef

1 small onion, chopped

½ cup golden raisins

1 tablespoon capers, rinsed and drained

2 cloves garlic, minced

1 teaspoon dried oregano

¼ teaspoon salt

¼ teaspoon black pepper

¼ cup grated Romano cheese

4 red bell peppers

2 cups tomato juice

**COOK** the rice according to package directions.

**HEAT** a large nonstick skillet over medium-high heat. Crumble in the beef and cook, stirring with a wooden spoon to break up any chunks, for about 4 minutes, or until no longer pink. Cook and stir the onion, raisins, capers, garlic, oregano, salt, and black pepper for about 5 minutes, or until the onion begins to soften. Stir in the rice. Remove from the heat and stir in the cheese.

**SLICE** the tops from the bell peppers. Remove and discard the seeds and ribs. Divide the beef mixture among the peppers. Set the peppers in a pot just large enough to hold them snugly. Add the tomato juice. Cover and bring to a boil over medium-high heat. Reduce the heat to medium-low. Cook for about 35 minutes, or until the peppers are tender. Serve topped with the pan sauce.

Total time: 1 hour  ✱  Makes 4 servings

Per serving: 325 calories, 25 g protein, 39 g carbohydrates, 7 g total fat, 4 g saturated fat, 5 g fiber, 579 mg sodium

Convenience foods often get a bad rap, but items like instant brown rice enable us to incorporate healthful whole grains into our meals with little time or effort.

## NUTRITION NEWS TO USE

If you're still eating white rice, here's yet another reason to get on the brown bandwagon: Eating brown rice just twice a week could lower your risk of type 2 diabetes by 11 percent, according to a study in the *Archives of Internal Medicine*. Brown rice has more fiber, magnesium, and other nutrients shown to reduce the risk, and it causes your blood sugar to rise less rapidly after a meal than white rice does, says lead study author Qi Sun, MD, ScD. If you don't like the taste of brown rice, try blending the two varieties until your palate becomes accustomed to it. Replacing about ⅓ cup of cooked white rice with brown every day was associated with a 16 percent lower risk.

# Pork Tenderloin with Nectarine Sage Relish

2 teaspoons Dijon mustard

2 cloves garlic, minced

1¼ pounds pork tenderloin

2 tablespoons lemon juice

2 teaspoons honey

¼ teaspoon salt

¼ teaspoon pepper

2 large nectarines, cut into ½" pieces

1 small red onion, finely chopped

1 tablespoon finely chopped fresh sage

IN a small bowl, stir together the mustard and garlic. Place the pork on a cutting board or baking pan. Spread the mustard mixture all over the pork to coat. Let stand for 10 minutes.

MEANWHILE, in a medium bowl, whisk together the lemon juice, honey, salt, and pepper until the honey dissolves. Stir in the nectarines, onion, and sage.

LIGHTLY coat a grill or grill pan with cooking spray. Preheat the grill over medium-high heat.

GRILL the pork for 15 minutes, turning occasionally, or until a thermometer inserted in the center registers 145°F and the juices run clear. Let stand for 10 minutes before slicing. Serve with the relish.

Total time: 1 hour 5 minutes ❋ Makes 4 servings

Per serving: 228 calories, 31 g protein, 17 g carbohydrates, 4 g total fat, 2 g saturated fat, 3 g fiber, 286 mg sodium

The tenderloin is the most tender and leanest cut of pork you can buy. Plus, there's absolutely no waste because it's boneless.

## [ TAKE D WITH YOUR DINNER ]

Pop your D vitamin supplement with the largest meal of the day and you'll boost absorption by nearly 57 percent, finds new Cleveland Clinic research. Most of us don't get enough of this power nutrient, which may ward off cancer, boost immunity, lower diabetes risk, prevent back pain, and more.

# Pineapple-Glazed Pork Chops

½ cup pineapple juice

1 large clove garlic, minced

1 teaspoon Worcestershire sauce

¼ teaspoon dried thyme

¼ teaspoon salt

¼ teaspoon pepper

4 boneless center-cut pork loin chops (5 ounces each)

IN a glass or ceramic baking dish large enough to hold the chops, stir together the pineapple juice, garlic, Worcestershire sauce, thyme, salt, and pepper. Add the chops and turn several times to coat evenly. Cover and refrigerate, turning once, for 30 minutes.

COAT a grill rack with cooking spray. Preheat the grill to medium-high.

REMOVE the chops and discard the marinade. Grill, turning once, for 10 minutes, or until a thermometer inserted in the center of a chop registers 160°F and the juices run clear.

----

Total time: 45 minutes ✳ Makes 4 servings

Per serving: 199 calories, 32 g protein, 5 g carbohydrates, 5 g total fat, 2 g saturated fat, 0 g fiber, 231 mg sodium

Today's pork is bred to be leaner. The fruit juice–based marinade used here will guarantee that the meat stays moist and flavorful.

# Pork Souvlaki with Yogurt Sauce

1 tablespoon extra virgin olive oil

1 tablespoon lemon juice

2 cloves garlic, minced

1 pound pork tenderloin, trimmed of all visible fat, cut into 24 chunks

¾ cup fat-free plain yogurt

¼ small cucumber, finely chopped

1 tablespoon chopped fresh dill

¼ teaspoon salt, divided

1 onion, cut into 4 slices

4 plum tomatoes

4 multigrain pitas (6" diameter)

4 leaves romaine lettuce

**IN** a large bowl, whisk together the oil, lemon juice, and garlic. Add the pork and toss several times to coat. Cover and refrigerate, tossing occasionally, for 1 hour.

**MEANWHILE,** in a medium bowl, stir together the yogurt, cucumber, dill, and a pinch of the salt. Cover and refrigerate.

**PREHEAT** the grill to medium-high. Remove the pork and discard the marinade. Thread the pork onto 4 metal skewers. Sprinkle the onion with the remaining salt. Grill the onion and tomatoes, turning once, for about 12 minutes, or until tender. Grill the pork for about 8 minutes, turning frequently, or until a thermometer inserted in the center of a cube registers 145°F and the juices run clear. Remove to a platter.

**GRILL** the pitas for 1 minute per side, or until toasted. Remove to 4 plates. Divide the lettuce, pork, onion, and tomatoes among the pitas. Top with the yogurt sauce.

Total time: 1 hour 45 minutes  **✻**  Makes 4 servings

Per serving: 372 calories, 33 g protein, 44 g carbohydrates, 8 g total fat, 2 g saturated fat, 6 g fiber, 581 mg sodium

You can vary this master recipe by using turkey breast or cubed firm tofu in place of the pork.

# Penne with Broccoli Raab and Sausage

- 1 pound broccoli raab, coarsely chopped
- ½ pound whole grain penne
- 1½ tablespoons extra virgin olive oil
- ½ pound loose-packed sweet Italian sausage
- 6 cloves garlic, sliced
- 1 cup reduced-sodium chicken broth
- ½ teaspoon salt
- 1 tablespoon grated Parmesan cheese

**BRING** a large pot of water to a boil. Add the broccoli raab and cook for about 2 minutes, or until bright green and tender-crisp. With kitchen tongs or a slotted spoon, transfer the broccoli raab to a bowl of ice water to stop the cooking. Drain well and gently squeeze to remove any excess water. Return the water in the pot to a boil. Cook the pasta according to package directions. Drain.

**MEANWHILE,** heat the oil in a large nonstick skillet over medium-high heat. Cook the sausage, breaking it into smaller pieces with a wooden spoon, for about 5 minutes, or until no longer pink. Add the garlic and cook for about 2 minutes, or until lightly golden. Add the broth and bring to a boil. Cook for about 4 minutes, or until reduced by half. Stir in the broccoli raab and salt. Cook for 2 minutes, or until hot. Stir in the pasta and cheese.

---

Total time: 25 minutes ✱ Makes 4 servings

Per serving: 400 calories, 22 g protein, 51 g carbohydrates, 12 g total fat, 3 g saturated fat, 5 g fiber, 550 mg sodium

Not so long ago, the bittersweet green vegetable broccoli raab seemed exotic, but now it's a staple in supermarket produce bins. Milder broccoli—peeled, chopped stems and florets—can replace the broccoli raab, if you like.

# Spiced Orange Roast Leg of Lamb

¼ cup orange juice

1 tablespoon ground cumin

1 tablespoon chopped fresh parsley

2 teaspoons dried thyme

2 cloves garlic, minced

½ teaspoon salt

½ teaspoon pepper

1 boneless sirloin leg of lamb (3 pounds), tied

**PREHEAT** the oven to 350°F. Coat a shallow roasting pan with cooking spray.

**IN** a small bowl, stir together the orange juice, cumin, parsley, thyme, garlic, salt, and pepper to form a paste. Cut ½"-deep slits in the thickest parts of the roast. Fill the slits with half of the seasoning paste, pressing the mixture in with your finger. Rub the remaining paste all over the roast.

**LIGHTLY** coat a large skillet with cooking spray. Heat over medium-high heat. Cook the roast, turning as needed, for about 10 minutes, or until well browned all over. Remove to the roasting pan.

**ROAST** for at least 1 hour, or until a thermometer inserted in the center registers 145°F for medium-rare/160°F for medium/165°F for well-done. Let stand for 10 minutes before slicing.

Total time: 1 hour 30 minutes ✱ Makes 8 servings

Per serving: 227 calories, 35 g protein, 2 g carbohydrates, 8 g total fat, 3 g saturated fat, 1 g fiber, 261 mg sodium

Mediterranean seasonings work their magic on this special-occasion leg of lamb roast.

# Braised Chicken and Cannellini Beans

6 boneless, skinless chicken breasts (4 ounces each), halved

Flour for dusting

2 tablespoons extra virgin olive oil, divided

1 onion, chopped

3 cloves garlic, minced

3 small red potatoes, cubed (1¼ pounds)

2 carrots, thinly sliced

2 ribs celery, chopped

1 teaspoon dried oregano

1 can (15 ounces) cannellini beans, rinsed and drained

1 can (14.5 ounces) no-salt-added crushed tomatoes

1 cup reduced-sodium chicken broth

¼ teaspoon salt

¼ teaspoon pepper

2 tablespoons chopped fresh parsley

**PREHEAT** the oven to 425°F. Coat a large baking dish with cooking spray.

**DUST** the chicken with flour to coat. Shake off excess. Heat 1 tablespoon of the oil in a large nonstick skillet over medium-high heat. Cook the chicken, turning once, for about 10 minutes, or until lightly browned. Remove to the baking dish.

**REDUCE** the heat to medium. Stir and cook the onion, garlic, and the remaining 1 tablespoon oil for about 6 minutes, or until lightly browned. Stir in the potatoes, carrots, celery, and oregano. Cook, stirring occasionally, for about 10 minutes, or until the vegetables are lightly browned. Stir in the beans, tomatoes, broth, salt, and pepper. Cook for about 2 minutes, or until bubbling. Ladle into the baking dish.

**BAKE** for about 30 minutes, or until browned and bubbling. Sprinkle with the parsley.

------------------------------------

Total time: 1 hour 10 minutes ✱ Makes 6 servings

Per serving: 341 calories, 31 g protein, 35 g carbohydrates, 8 g total fat, 1 g saturated fat, 7 g fiber, 497 mg sodium

Oven-braised dishes like this one reheat beautifully, so you can make it several days ahead in anticipation of a night when you don't have time to cook. Reheat in a large covered pot over medium heat, stirring occasionally, for about 10 minutes.

# Chicken Piccata with Rice

2 teaspoons olive oil

4 boneless, skinless chicken breast halves (4 ounces each)

1¼ cups instant brown rice

1¼ cups reduced-sodium chicken broth

¼ cup finely chopped fresh parsley

¼ cup lemon juice

2 tablespoons capers, rinsed, drained, and chopped

½ teaspoon dried oregano

2 tablespoons chopped pine nuts or almonds, toasted (page 98)

**COAT** a large nonstick skillet with cooking spray. Heat the oil over medium heat. Cook the chicken, turning once, for about 10 minutes, or until lightly browned.

**ADD** the rice, broth, parsley, lemon juice, capers, and oregano. Bring to a boil. Reduce the heat to medium-low.

**COVER** and cook for 10 minutes, or until a thermometer inserted in the thickest portion of the chicken registers 165°F and the juices run clear. Remove from the heat and let stand for 5 minutes. Sprinkle with the nuts.

------------------------------------------------

Total time: 30 minutes ❋ Makes 4 servings

Per serving: 252 calories, 27 g protein, 22 g carbohydrates, 6 g total fat, 1 g saturated fat, 2 g fiber, 405 mg sodium

Serve this Italian specialty with Roasted Broccoli with Orange (page 247).

# Chicken with Grapefruit

- 2 tablespoons olive oil
- 4 boneless, skinless chicken breast halves (4 ounces each)
- ½ teaspoon dried thyme
- ½ teaspoon salt
- ¼ teaspoon pepper
- ⅓ cup reduced-sodium chicken broth
- ¼ cup grapefruit juice
- 2 teaspoons honey
- 3 ounces trimmed watercress
- 2 grapefruit, cut into segments

**HEAT** the oil in a skillet over medium-high heat. Season the chicken with the thyme, salt, and pepper. Cook, turning once, for about 12 minutes, or until browned. Add the broth, grapefruit juice, and honey. Reduce the heat to medium-low and cook for about 5 minutes, or until the liquid is reduced to ⅓ cup.

**DIVIDE** the watercress and grapefruit among 4 plates. Top with the chicken. Drizzle with the pan juices.

Total time: 25 minutes ✶ Makes 4 servings

Per serving: 266 calories, 27 g protein, 15 g carbohydrates, 10 g total fat, 2 g saturated fat, 2 g fiber, 438 mg sodium

Release tangy grapefruit from its early morning rut with this simple, elegant dinner dish.

---

## SUPERFOOD SPOTLIGHT: GRAPEFRUIT

Grapefruit is a terrific source of vitamins A and $B_5$, potassium, folate, and fiber. And it's loaded with cancer-fighting lycopene. It is at its sweetest, juiciest, and cheapest in January and February, so stock up! Look for fruit that feels heavy for its size and has fine-grained rather than coarse skin. Both characteristics indicate lots of juicy flesh. A half grapefruit has just 53 waistline-friendly calories to boot.

# Peanut-Glazed Chicken Tenders with Green Sauce

1 pound chicken breast tenders

¼ cup Thai peanut sauce

½ cup fresh baby spinach

¼ cup fresh cilantro

¼ cup panko bread crumbs

2 scallions, white and green parts, cut into 1" pieces

1 tablespoon olive oil

½ jalapeño chile pepper, seeded (optional), wear plastic gloves when handling

⅛ teaspoon salt

COAT a grill rack or broiler-pan rack with cooking spray. Preheat the grill or broiler to medium-high.

IN a glass or ceramic baking dish, toss the chicken with the peanut sauce. Let stand for 10 minutes.

IN a food processor, combine the spinach, cilantro, bread crumbs, scallions, oil, jalapeño pepper (if using), and salt. Process for about 1 minute, or until a rough paste forms. If needed, add a few drops of water to loosen the mixture.

REMOVE the chicken to the grill rack or broiler pan. Grill or broil, turning several times, for 15 minutes, or until no longer pink and the juices run clear. Serve with the green sauce.

----

Total time: 30 minutes  ✳  Makes 4 servings

Per serving: 192 calories, 27 g protein, 8 g carbohydrates, 6 g total fat, 2 g saturated fat, 1 g fiber, 227 mg sodium

Serve Cajun Sweet Potato Fries (page 240) and a tossed green salad on the side.

# Chicken Spiedini
# with Balsamic Dipping Sauce

½ cup balsamic vinegar

1 tablespoon extra virgin olive oil

2 cloves garlic, minced

1 tablespoon grated Parmesan cheese

1 pound boneless, skinless chicken breasts, cut into 1" chunks

10 scallions, cut into 1" pieces

1 large red bell pepper, cut into 1" pieces

1 large sprig fresh rosemary, broken into pieces

**PREHEAT** the broiler. Lightly coat a broiler-pan rack with cooking spray.

**IN** a small bowl, whisk together the vinegar, oil, and garlic. Pour half into a 13" × 9" glass or ceramic dish. Stir the cheese into the remainder and set aside for the dipping sauce.

**THREAD** the chicken, scallions, and pepper onto 8 skewers (8" long). Place in the dish, along with the rosemary, and rotate several times to coat with the marinade. Let stand for 10 minutes.

**REMOVE** the skewers to the broiler pan. Broil, turning and basting occasionally with the marinade, for about 10 minutes, or until the chicken is no longer pink and the juices run clear. Serve with the dipping sauce.

Total time: 25 minutes ✱ Makes 4 servings

Per serving: 215 calories, 26 g protein, 10 g carbohydrates, 7 g total fat, 2 g saturated fat, 2 g fiber, 181 mg sodium

If using wooden skewers, soak them in water for 30 minutes before cooking so they don't char under the broiler flame.

# Creole Chicken and Sausage

2 teaspoons canola oil

1 bunch scallions, white and green parts, sliced

1 large rib celery, sliced

1 small red or green bell pepper, coarsely chopped

1 pound boneless, skinless chicken breasts, cut into ¾" cubes

1 can (14.5 ounces) reduced-sodium chicken broth

1¼ cups instant brown rice

2 ounces low-fat smoked turkey sausage, chopped

¾ teaspoon dried thyme

¼ teaspoon ground red pepper

1 can (14.5 ounces) diced tomatoes

HEAT the oil in a large nonstick skillet over medium heat. Cook and stir the scallions, celery, and bell pepper for 3 minutes, or until the pepper is tender.

STIR in the chicken and cook for 4 minutes, or until opaque. Stir in the broth, rice, sausage, thyme, and ground red pepper. Bring to a simmer. Reduce the heat to medium-low and cook, stirring occasionally, for 3 minutes.

STIR in the tomatoes and cook just until the mixture comes to a simmer. Turn off the heat, cover, and let stand for 5 minutes, or until the rice is tender. Stir gently.

--------------------------------------------

Total time: 25 minutes  ✱  Makes 6 servings

Per serving: 324 calories, 29 g protein, 38 g carbohydrates, 6 g total fat, 2 g saturated fat, 3 g fiber, 771 mg sodium

## NUTRITION NEWS TO USE

Recent research found that 47 percent of people had too-low levels of vitamin C, even though just a 4-ounce glass of orange juice delivers nearly all you need each day. Those with the lowest levels were likelier to have higher BMIs, waist circumferences, and blood pressure than people with adequate C. The vitamin protects against inflammation, and your body uses it to build fat-burning compounds. Excellent sources include red bell peppers, broccoli, cauliflower, and even romaine lettuce. Many multivitamins contain the recommended daily intake, so you don't need a separate C supplement.

# Honey-Roasted Turkey Breast

- 1 **bone-in turkey breast half (2½ pounds)**
- ⅓ **cup honey**
- ¾ **teaspoon ground cinnamon**
- 1 **cup reduced-sodium chicken broth**, divided

**PREHEAT** the oven to 350°F. Coat a shallow roasting pan with cooking spray. Trim all visible fat and excess skin from the turkey breast. Leave just enough skin to cover the top of the breast. Place the turkey, skin side up, in the roasting pan. Pour the honey over the turkey. Lift the skin and spread with a spatula to evenly coat the breast. Sprinkle with the cinnamon, rubbing it under the skin. Pour ⅔ cup of the broth into the pan.

**ROAST** for 40 minutes. Carefully remove and discard the skin. Add up to ⅓ cup of the remaining broth, if needed, to prevent the glaze in the pan from burning. Roast for 20 minutes, or until a thermometer inserted in the thickest portion registers 170°F and the juices run clear. Remove the turkey and let stand for 10 minutes. Pour the pan juices into a serving dish. Skim off and discard any fat. Slice the turkey and serve with the pan juices.

-------------------------------------------------------------

Total time: 1 hour 20 minutes  ✱  Makes 6 servings

Per serving: 225 calories, 37 g protein, 16 g carbohydrates, 1 g total fat, 0 g saturated fat, 0 g fiber, 149 mg sodium

Roasting turkey breast to make your own cold cuts is a smarter option than purchasing pricey deli meats, which are high in fat and sodium. Cool the breast, refrigerate overnight, and then cut into thin slices. Freeze in recipe-ready portions.

# San Antonio Turkey Fajitas

1 pound boneless, skinless turkey breast cutlets

2 tablespoons lime juice

3 cloves garlic, minced

2 teaspoons Worcestershire sauce

½ teaspoon ground cumin

½ serrano chile pepper, seeded and finely chopped (optional), wear plastic gloves when handling

⅛ teaspoon salt

2 large red or green bell peppers, thickly sliced

1 large red onion, cut into ½"-thick rounds

2 teaspoons olive oil

4 whole wheat tortillas (8" diameter)

Salsa (optional)

IN a resealable plastic bag, combine the turkey, lime juice, garlic, Worcestershire sauce, cumin, and serrano pepper (if using). Seal the bag and massage to coat the turkey well. Let stand for 20 minutes.

LIGHTLY coat a grill rack with cooking spray. Preheat the grill to medium-high.

IN a medium bowl, toss together the bell peppers, onion, oil, and salt. Using a grill basket or grill topper, grill the vegetables, turning occasionally, for about 18 minutes, or until lightly charred. Remove the peppers and onion to a platter.

REMOVE the turkey and discard the marinade. Grill the turkey for about 3 minutes per side, or until no longer pink. Remove to a cutting board.

GRILL the tortillas for about 30 seconds per side, or until warm and lightly browned.

SLICE the turkey into strips. Place on the platter with the vegetables and serve with the tortillas and salsa (if using).

----

Total time: 50 minutes ✱ Makes 4 servings

Per serving: 323 calories, 33 g protein, 31 g carbohydrates, 6 g total fat, 1 g saturated fat, 4 g fiber, 358 mg sodium

## [ METABOLISM BOOSTER: HOT PEPPERS ]

Capsaicin, the compound that gives hot chile peppers their kick, raises your core body temperature, causing you to burn more calories, according to the *International Journal of Obesity*. Hotter peppers have a greater effect, so use the spiciest type you can stand in chili, curries, or sauces.

# Mediterranean Turkey Stew with Olives

1 tablespoon extra virgin olive oil

1¼ pounds boneless, skinless turkey breast, cut into 1" cubes

2 zucchini, cut into ½" cubes

1 red onion, chopped

2 cloves garlic, minced

1 teaspoon ground cumin

1 can (14.5 ounces) no-salt-added crushed tomatoes

1 tablespoon grated orange peel

½ teaspoon salt

¼ teaspoon pepper

12 pitted medium green olives, halved

3 tablespoons chopped fresh cilantro or parsley

HEAT the oil in a large nonstick skillet over medium-high heat. Cook the turkey, turning occasionally, for about 4 minutes, or until lightly browned. Remove to a plate.

REDUCE the heat to medium. Cook and stir the zucchini, onion, garlic, and cumin for about 3 minutes, or until the onion is softened. Stir in the tomatoes, orange peel, salt, and pepper. Bring to a simmer. Return the turkey and accumulated juices to the pan. Cook for 5 minutes. Stir in the olives and cilantro or parsley.

REDUCE the heat to low, cover, and cook for 10 minutes, or until the turkey is no longer pink and the juices run clear.

------------------------------------------------

Total time: 30 minutes ✳ Makes 4 servings

Per serving: 275 calories, 38 g protein, 14 g carbohydrates, 7 g total fat, 1 g saturated fat, 3 g fiber, 515 mg sodium

Purchase ground spices from the bulk section of your supermarket or in ethnic groceries, where the prices are much lower than prepackaged bottles. Store them in a cool, dry spot.

# Baked Turkey Cutlets
# with Peppers and Mushrooms

1¼ pounds turkey breast cutlets

1 onion, thinly sliced

2 red or green bell peppers, thinly sliced

8 ounces fresh mushrooms, thinly sliced

½ teaspoon dried thyme

½ teaspoon dried sage

⅛ teaspoon salt

⅛ teaspoon black pepper

**PREHEAT** the oven to 350°F. Coat an 8" × 8" baking dish with cooking spray. Place the turkey, onion, bell peppers, mushrooms, thyme, sage, salt, and black pepper in the dish.

**COVER** with foil and bake for 30 minutes, or until the turkey is no longer pink.

---

Total time: 40 minutes ✳ Makes 6 servings

Per serving: 130 calories, 25 g protein, 5 g carbohydrates, 1 g total fat, 0 g saturated fat, 2 g fiber, 135 mg sodium

This meal cooks itself, giving you the gift of an extra half hour for a quick walk or workout.

# Chai Scallops with Bok Choy

- 4 heads baby bok choy, quartered lengthwise or halved if small
- 1 tablespoon minced fresh ginger
- ⅓ cup boiling water
- 2 bags chai tea
- 2 teaspoons canola oil, divided
- 1 pound sea scallops, halved through the middle
- ¼ teaspoon salt
- ⅓ cup canned light coconut milk
- 1 lime, cut into 4 wedges

**PLACE** a steamer basket in a large pot with 2" water. Bring to a boil over high heat. Place the bok choy and ginger in the basket. Cover and steam for about 4 minutes, or until the bok choy is tender but still firm when pierced with a sharp knife.

**MEANWHILE,** combine the water and tea bags in a cup. Let steep for 3 minutes. Discard the tea bags.

**HEAT** 1 teaspoon of the oil in a large skillet over medium-high heat. Pat the scallops dry and sprinkle with the salt. Cook half of the scallops, turning once, for 4 minutes, or until opaque. Remove to a plate. Repeat with the remaining 1 teaspoon oil and scallops. Remove to a plate.

**STIR** the tea and coconut milk into the pan. Cook and swirl for about 2 minutes, or until the mixture thickens slightly. Divide the sauce among 4 shallow bowls. Top with the bok choy and scallops. Serve with the lime wedges.

Total time: 20 minutes ✽ Makes 4 servings

Per serving: 151 calories, 21 g protein, 7 g carbohydrates, 5 g total fat, 1 g saturated fat, 1 g fiber, 389 mg sodium

Using moderate amounts of decadent ingredients such as light coconut milk helps keep us satisfied and focused on our health goals.

# Seafood and Okra Jambalaya

2 teaspoons olive oil

2 ounces chorizo sausage, finely chopped

1 package (10 ounces) frozen cut okra

1 onion, chopped

1 red bell pepper, chopped

3 ribs celery, chopped

1½ teaspoons salt-free Creole seasoning

1 can (14.5 ounces) no-salt-added diced tomatoes

1 can (14.5 ounces) reduced-sodium chicken broth

1 cup instant brown rice

1½ pounds peeled and deveined medium shrimp

½ pound catfish fillet, cut into chunks

HEAT the oil in a large pot over medium-high heat. Cook and stir the chorizo for 2 minutes, or until starting to brown. Stir in the okra, onion, pepper, and celery. Cook, stirring occasionally, for about 8 minutes, or until softened. Add the seasoning and cook for 30 seconds. Stir in the tomatoes, broth, and rice. Bring to a boil.

REDUCE the heat to medium-low, cover, and cook for 15 minutes to allow the flavors to blend. Stir in the shrimp and catfish and cook for 5 minutes, or until the liquid is absorbed, the fish flakes easily, and the shrimp are opaque. Remove from the heat and let stand for about 5 minutes for flavors to blend.

Total time: 50 minutes  ✱  Makes 6 servings

Per serving: 310 calories, 33 g protein, 23 g carbohydrates, 10 g total fat, 3 g saturated fat, 3 g fiber, 610 mg sodium

With this Louisiana classic and a tossed green salad, supper is served.

# Roasted Salmon with Mustard-Dill Glaze

- 4 center-cut salmon fillets (4 ounces each)
- 3 tablespoons reduced-fat mayonnaise
- 1 tablespoon stone-ground mustard
- 1 tablespoon chopped fresh dill
- 1½ teaspoons packed light brown sugar
- 1 teaspoon lemon juice
- ½ teaspoon salt
- ⅛ teaspoon pepper

**PREHEAT** the oven to 400°F. Line a baking sheet with foil. Place the fillets on the pan.

**IN** a small dish, whisk together the mayonnaise, mustard, dill, sugar, lemon juice, salt, and pepper. Spread evenly over the fillets.

**ROAST** for about 12 minutes, or until the fish is opaque.

---

Total time: 20 minutes ❋ Makes 4 servings

Per serving: 261 calories, 23 g protein, 3 g carbohydrates, 17 g total fat, 4 g saturated fat, 0 g fiber, 504 mg sodium

Salmon, especially that caught in the wild, is rich with heart-healthy omega-3 fatty acids.

# Swordfish with Sun-Dried Tomatoes and Rosemary

1½ pounds swordfish steak, cut into 1" cubes

Instant flour or all-purpose flour, for coating

¼ teaspoon salt, divided

Pepper

4 teaspoons extra virgin olive oil, divided

1 zucchini or yellow squash, halved lengthwise and thinly sliced

3 ounces fresh lima or fava beans (¾ cup)

½ small onion, finely chopped

2 cloves garlic, minced

2 teaspoons minced fresh rosemary

1 cup dry-pack sun-dried tomatoes, halved

½ cup fresh or frozen and thawed corn kernels

DUST the fish lightly with flour, shaking off excess. Sprinkle with ⅛ teaspoon of the salt and season lightly with pepper.

HEAT 2 teaspoons of the oil in a large nonstick skillet over medium-high heat.

ADD the fish. Cook for about 6 minutes, turning as needed, or until golden brown on all sides and the fish is just opaque. Remove to a plate and cover.

REDUCE the heat to medium and add the remaining 2 teaspoons oil to the pan.

COOK and stir the zucchini or yellow squash, lima or fava beans, onion, garlic, and rosemary for about 5 minutes, or until the vegetables are softened. Stir in the tomatoes and corn. Cook for about 3 minutes, or until the tomatoes and corn are heated through. Return the fish to the pan and sprinkle with the remaining ⅛ teaspoon salt and pepper to taste. Cook for 30 seconds, or until the fish is heated through.

Total time: 25 minutes  ✻  Makes 4 servings

Per serving: 412 calories, 42 g protein, 34 g carbohydrates, 13 g total fat, 3 g saturated fat, 7 g fiber, 593 mg sodium

Halibut or shark can stand in for the swordfish in this hearty skillet supper.

# Orange Roughy Calypso

2 cups instant brown rice

1 cup reduced-sodium chicken broth

1 yellow bell pepper, cut into thin strips

1 bunch scallions, all parts, sliced diagonally into 1" pieces

4 slices lime

1 tablespoon finely chopped fresh cilantro

¼ teaspoon curry powder

4 skinless orange roughy fillets (4 ounces each and ½" thick)

**COOK** the rice according to package directions.

**MEANWHILE,** in a large nonstick skillet over high heat, stir together the broth, pepper, scallions, lime, cilantro, and curry powder. Cover and bring to a boil. Place the fish in the pan. Reduce the heat to medium-low. Cover and cook for about 10 minutes, or until the fish flakes easily. Discard the lime.

---

Total time: 20 minutes　✳︎　Makes 4 servings

Per serving: 322 calories, 25 g protein, 50 g carbohydrates, 2 g total fat, 0 g saturated fat, 2 g fiber, 180 mg sodium

Other white-fleshed fish work well in this recipe. Try turbot, cod, tilapia, or catfish.

## GOTTA TRY IT: COOKWARE THAT SAVES CALORIES

More flavorful meals with less fat and in less time—that's the promise of 360 Cookware. These pots and pans use vapor cooking, which captures your food's natural liquid as it vaporizes, so you don't need to add oil or butter. The lid forms a seal, so the contents cook from all sides, and layers of high-grade metals conduct heat so efficiently that your meal cooks much faster. But can food with no added fat taste good? *Prevention* testers found fish and chicken "amazingly good." Prices start at $80 (www.360cookware.com), but it's worth the splurge.

# Poached Flounder Italian-Style

1 cup reduced-sodium chicken broth

1 tomato, chopped

1 small green bell pepper, cut into strips

4 ounces fresh mushrooms, sliced

1 small onion, thinly sliced

1 clove garlic, minced

2 teaspoons dried Italian herb seasoning

⅛ teaspoon black pepper

4 skinless flounder fillets (about 4 ounces each)

2 tablespoons grated Parmesan cheese

**IN** a large skillet over medium-high heat, stir together the broth, tomato, bell pepper, mushrooms, onion, garlic, seasoning, and black pepper. Cover and bring to a boil.

**PLACE** the fish in the pan. Reduce the heat to medium-low. Cover and cook for about 10 minutes, or until the fish flakes easily. Sprinkle with the cheese.

------

Total time: 20 minutes * Makes 4 servings

Per serving: 141 calories, 24 g protein, 5 g carbohydrates, 3 g total fat, 1 g saturated fat, 1 g fiber, 288 mg sodium

Don't fear preparing fish at home. In this recipe, flounder fillets cook in just 10 minutes in a savory broth mixture.

[ **QUICK TIP: ALL CHOKED UP**
**41%** The amount of the daily goal for fiber you get in one medium cooked artichoke ]

# Portuguese Mussel Stew

2 tablespoons extra virgin olive oil

1 small onion, chopped

3 cloves garlic, minced

1½ teaspoons paprika

½ cup white wine or reduced-sodium chicken broth

½ cup reduced-sodium chicken broth or water

1 cup canned crushed tomatoes

¼ teaspoon salt

4 pounds mussels

¼ cup chopped fresh cilantro

**HEAT** the oil in a large pot over medium heat. Cook and stir the onion, garlic, and paprika for 3 minutes, or until the onion softens. Add the wine and broth or water. Increase the heat to high. Bring to a boil for 3 minutes. Add the tomatoes and salt. Bring to a boil. Stir in the mussels. Cover and cook for about 8 minutes, or until the mussels open. Discard any shells that don't open. Sprinkle with the cilantro.

Total time: 20 minutes ✱ Makes 4 servings

Per serving: 250 calories, 20 g protein, 13 g carbohydrates, 11 g total fat, 2 g saturated fat, 2 g fiber, 640 mg sodium

To clean mussels, run them under cold water, scrubbing gently with a vegetable brush. Discard any with broken shells or shells that remain open after being lightly tapped. As you go, pull off and discard the "beard" (the fibrous piece that sometimes remains attached to the shell).

## NUTRITION NEWS TO USE

Researchers used to think that only specialty mushrooms such as shiitakes and maitakes improve heart health. But in lab tests, extracts from common white button, cremini, and oyster mushrooms also helped reduce chronic inflammation that can lead to cardiovascular disease. So if you're not sure about the fancy ones, go ahead and stick with your favorite variety. At 20 to 30 calories per cup, all these mushrooms are good for your ticker—and your waistline.

# Thai Stir-Fried Shrimp and Crispy Vegetables

4 teaspoons canola oil, divided

1 tablespoon Thai fish sauce

3 cloves garlic, minced

1½ pounds medium peeled and deveined shrimp

1 tablespoon finely chopped fresh ginger

8 ounces fresh mushrooms, sliced

1 large yellow bell pepper, cut into thin strips

8 ounces sugar snap peas or snow peas

4 scallions, cut into 1" pieces diagonally

2 tablespoons lime juice

2 tablespoons fresh Thai basil leaves, slivered (optional)

Asian chili paste (optional)

IN a large bowl, whisk together 2 teaspoons of the oil, the fish sauce, and garlic. Toss with the shrimp.

LIGHTLY coat a large skillet or wok with cooking spray. Heat over high heat. Cook and toss the shrimp for 2 minutes, or until opaque. Remove to a plate.

HEAT the remaining 2 teaspoons oil in the pan over high heat. Cook and stir the ginger for 30 seconds. Add the mushrooms, pepper, snap peas or snow peas, and scallions.

COOK, tossing occasionally, for about 4 minutes, or until the vegetables are tender-crisp. Stir in the shrimp, lime juice, and basil (if using). Pass the chili paste (if using) at the table.

--------------------------------------------

Total time: 20 minutes  ✱  Makes 4 servings

Per serving: 259 calories, 35 g protein, 13 g carbohydrates, 8 g total fat, 1 g saturated fat, 3 g fiber, 558 mg sodium

The profusion of international flavorings in supermarkets means a whole new world of opportunities for cooking healthfully.

# Chioccicle with Salmon and Goat Cheese

¾ pound skinless salmon fillet

1 tablespoon balsamic vinegar

½ pound whole grain chioccicle

1 cup frozen baby peas or edamame

2 ounces crumbled goat cheese

¼ cup chopped fresh mint or basil

1 scallion, white part only, minced

¼ teaspoon salt

Pepper

**PREHEAT** the broiler. Cover a broiler pan with foil and lightly coat the rack with cooking spray. Place the fish on the rack and brush with the vinegar. Broil for about 10 minutes, or until the fish is opaque. Remove to a large bowl. When cool enough to handle, break into bite-size pieces.

**MEANWHILE,** cook the pasta according to package directions, adding the peas or edamame during the last 2 minutes of cooking. Reserve ¼ cup of the pasta cooking water before draining. Drain the pasta mixture and add to the bowl, along with the cheese, mint or basil, scallion, salt, and the reserved cooking water. Toss to coat. Season liberally with pepper.

Total time: 15 minutes ✱ Makes 4 servings

Per serving: 440 calories, 30 g protein, 41 g carbohydrates, 17 g total fat, 6 g saturated fat, 9 g fiber, 270 mg sodium

The dried pasta chioccicle (key-oh-chee-olay) is as much fun to pronounce as it is to eat. If you can't find it at your market, replace it with penne, rotini, or campanelle pasta.

# Pasta Puttanesca

12 ounces linguine or spaghetti

1 tablespoon olive oil

1 small onion, chopped

2 cloves garlic, minced

1 can (28 ounces) no-salt-added diced tomatoes

10 kalamata olives, pitted and chopped

2 teaspoons rinsed and drained capers

½ teaspoon dried oregano

⅛ teaspoon red-pepper flakes

2 tablespoons grated Parmesan cheese (optional)

COOK the pasta according to package directions.

MEANWHILE, heat the oil in a large nonstick skillet over medium heat. Cook and stir the onion and garlic for about 3 minutes, or until the onion is tender. Stir in the tomatoes, olives, capers, oregano, and pepper flakes. Bring to a boil. Reduce the heat to low and simmer for about 12 minutes, or until the sauce thickens slightly.

DRAIN the pasta and place in a large serving bowl. Add the sauce and toss to mix well. Sprinkle with the cheese (if using).

Total time: 20 minutes ✳ Makes 4 servings

Per serving: 433 calories, 15 g protein, 76 g carbohydrates, 8 g total fat, 2 g saturated fat, 5 g fiber, 262 mg sodium

Keep all of the ingredients for this zesty main dish on hand and you can create a fabulous meal that fits into your eating plan in less time than you could get pizza delivered.

## QUICK TIP: COOK FROM THE CUPBOARD

Keep your pantry, refrigerator, and freezer stocked with quick-cook staples. If you already have ingredients such as canned beans, stock, and tuna; dried pasta and grains; grated cheese; and frozen veggie blends, you won't even need to stop at the market.

# Italian Lentil and Broccoli Stew

1 small onion, finely chopped

1 small carrot, finely chopped

2 cloves garlic, minced

2 teaspoons olive oil

2 cups reduced-sodium
   vegetable broth or water

1 cup dried brown lentils

1 teaspoon dried oregano

¼ teaspoon red-pepper flakes

2 pounds broccoli florets
   (4 cups)

16 large pitted green olives,
   slivered

4 teaspoons shredded
   Parmesan cheese

**IN** a medium saucepan over medium heat, combine the onion, carrot, garlic, and oil. Cover and cook for about 5 minutes, or until the vegetables start to soften.

**STIR** in the broth or water, lentils, oregano, and pepper flakes. Cover and bring almost to a boil. Reduce the heat to medium-low and cook for about 20 minutes, or until the lentils are tender.

**ADD** the broccoli. Cover and simmer for about 5 minutes, or until the broccoli is tender-crisp. Stir in the olives. Add more water, if necessary, to thin the stew to the desired consistency. Sprinkle with the cheese.

------

Total time: 40 minutes  ✳  Makes 4 servings

Per serving: 249 calories, 15 g protein, 39 g carbohydrates, 6 g total fat,
1 g saturated fat, 12 g fiber, 310 mg sodium

Lentils are a bargain whether you're watching your waistline or your budget. Packed with protein and fiber—and virtually no fat—they cost just pennies.

# Zucchini and Spinach Lasagna

9 lasagna noodles (5.5 ounces)

1 tablespoon extra virgin olive oil

1 zucchini, sliced

16 ounces reduced-fat ricotta cheese

1 egg

¼ teaspoon salt

⅛ teaspoon pepper

1 jar (16 ounces) pasta sauce

1 package (10 ounces) frozen chopped spinach, thawed and squeezed dry

½ cup fresh basil, loosely torn

¼ cup grated Romano cheese

¼ cup shredded reduced-fat mozzarella cheese

**PREHEAT** the oven to 350°F. Coat a 13" × 9" baking dish with cooking spray.

**COOK** the noodles according to package directions. Drain and rinse with cold water. Drain and set aside.

**HEAT** the oil in a medium skillet over medium heat. Cook the zucchini, stirring occasionally, for 5 minutes, or until tender-crisp. Remove from the heat and set aside.

**IN** a medium bowl, stir together the ricotta, egg, salt, and pepper.

**PLACE** 3 lasagna noodles in the baking dish. Spread ¾ cup of the sauce over the noodles. Top with half of the ricotta mixture, half of the spinach, half of the zucchini, half of the basil, and half of the Romano. Repeat the layering. Top with the remaining 3 noodles. Spread the remaining sauce over the noodles and sprinkle with the mozzarella.

**COVER** with foil and bake for 25 minutes. Uncover and bake for 20 minutes, or until hot and bubbly. Let stand for 10 minutes.

----

Total time: 1 hour 15 minutes  ✱  Makes 12 servings

Per serving: 155 calories, 9 g protein, 16 g carbohydrates, 5 g total fat, 2 g saturated fat, 1 g fiber, 361 mg sodium

Keep a lasagna in the freezer for healthy meal insurance. Assemble it in a freezer-to-oven baking dish. On evenings when you work late, all you have to do is pop it in the oven when you get home. The baking time may increase by about 10 minutes.

# Penne with Garden Veggies

8 ounces whole grain ridged penne

2 teaspoons extra virgin olive oil

1 onion, halved and thinly sliced

¼ green bell pepper, thinly slivered

3 cloves garlic, minced

1 large zucchini, shredded

1 cup red or yellow cherry or grape tomatoes, halved

¼ teaspoon salt

⅛ teaspoon black pepper

½ cup reduced-fat ricotta cheese

2 tablespoons chopped fresh parsley

COOK the pasta according to package directions. Reserve 2 tablespoons of the cooking water before draining. Set aside.

IN a large nonstick skillet, heat the oil over medium heat. Cook and stir the onion, bell pepper, and garlic for 3 minutes, or until the onion is softened.

ADD the zucchini, tomatoes, salt, black pepper, pasta, and the reserved pasta cooking water. Toss to combine. Dollop with the cheese. Cook and toss for about 1 minute to coat the pasta. Sprinkle with the parsley.

Total time: 20 minutes   ✱   Makes 4 servings

Per serving: 268 calories, 12 g protein, 45 g carbohydrates, 5 g total fat, 1 g saturated fat, 9 g fiber, 184 mg sodium

You'll turn to this dish time and time again when your garden—or the farmer's market—is bursting with fresh produce.

# Black Bean Pie

1 prepared pie crust
 (9" diameter)

1 can (16 ounces) black beans,
 rinsed and drained, divided

¼ cup reduced-sodium
 vegetable broth

2 teaspoons olive oil

1 red onion, chopped

3 cloves garlic, minced

2 teaspoons ground cumin

¼ teaspoon chili powder

3 drops hot-pepper sauce

3 eggs

½ cup salsa

½ cup shredded reduced-fat
 Monterey Jack cheese

**BAKE** the pie crust according to package directions. Set aside.

**PREHEAT** the oven to 400°F.

**IN** a food processor, combine ½ cup of the beans and the broth. Puree for about 1 minute, or until smooth. Set aside.

**HEAT** the oil in a medium nonstick skillet over medium heat. Cook the onion, stirring occasionally, for 4 minutes, or until soft. Stir in the garlic, cumin, chili powder, hot-pepper sauce, and the reserved pureed beans. Bring to a simmer. Stir in the remaining beans, cover, and simmer for 5 minutes, or until heated through. Remove from the heat and set aside to cool slightly. In a small bowl, beat the eggs with a fork. Stir into the bean mixture until blended. Pour into the pie crust.

**BAKE** for 10 minutes. Spread the salsa evenly over the bean mixture. Sprinkle with the cheese. Reduce the oven temperature to 325°F and bake for 15 minutes, or until the cheese is bubbly. Cool in the pan on a rack for 5 minutes.

Total time: 1 hour 10 minutes ✱ Makes 6 servings

Per serving: 303 calories, 9 g protein, 31 g carbohydrates, 16 g total fat, 6 g saturated fat, 3 g fiber, 549 mg sodium

Vegetarians and meat lovers alike will go crazy over this comforting legume pie with a Southwestern flair.

# Roasted Cauliflower Parmesan

1 small head cauliflower (about
  1 pound), cut into ⅓" slices

½ cup grated Parmesan cheese

⅛ teaspoon pepper

**PREHEAT** the oven to 350°F. Line a large rimmed baking sheet with foil. Coat lightly with cooking spray. Scatter the cauliflower on the pan. Sprinkle with the cheese.

**BAKE** for about 40 minutes, or until golden brown. Sprinkle with the pepper.

---

Total time: 45 minutes ✻ Makes 4 servings

Per serving: 47 calories, 4 g protein, 6 g carbohydrates, 2 g total fat, 1 g saturated fat, 3 g fiber, 116 mg sodium

Who says fresh vegetables are too much work to prepare? And if you start with precut cauliflower florets, this dish takes nearly zero effort.

[ **QUICK TIP: COLORFUL CRUCIFEROUS**
Cauliflower—a member of the cruciferous family of vegetables that includes broccoli, cabbage, and kale—comes in a rainbow of colors, from white and yellow to purple, and a cup provides at least 73 percent of the immune-boosting vitamin C you need daily. ]

# Cajun Sweet Potato Fries

4  **sweet potatoes (about
   1 pound), peeled**

1  **tablespoon olive oil**

2  **teaspoons Cajun seasoning**

**LIGHTLY** coat a grill rack or grill pan with cooking spray. Preheat the grill or pan to medium-high.

**CUT** the potatoes into ⅓"-thick fries. Remove to a large bowl. Toss together with the oil and seasoning until the potatoes are evenly coated.

**USING** a grill basket or grill topper, if necessary, grill the potatoes, turning occasionally, for about 10 minutes, or until tender and lightly browned.

-------------------------------------------

Total time: 20 minutes  ✳  Makes 4 servings

Per serving: 142 calories, 2 g protein, 26 g carbohydrates, 3 g total fat, 1 g saturated fat, 4 g fiber, 342 mg sodium

Sweet, spicy, and crisp: Cajun Sweet Potato Fries are a dieter's dream.

[ **QUICK TIP: POTATO POWER**
Sweet potatoes provide heart-healthy potassium, fiber, and vitamins (A and C). For the most eye and skin protection, choose ones that are deep orange. ]

# Sweet-and-Sour Brussels Sprouts

1 pound Brussels sprouts, halved

1 clove garlic, thinly sliced

1 tablespoon extra virgin olive oil

¼ teaspoon salt

⅛ teaspoon pepper

½ cup water

1 tablespoon packed light brown sugar

1 tablespoon cider vinegar

**PREHEAT** the oven to 425°F. Coat a 13" × 9" baking dish with cooking spray.

**TOSS** together the Brussels sprouts, garlic, oil, salt, and pepper in the pan.

**IN** a small bowl, whisk together the water, sugar, and vinegar to dissolve the sugar. Pour evenly over the sprouts.

**ROAST** for about 25 minutes, turning occasionally, or until the sprouts are lightly browned and tender when pierced with a sharp knife.

Total time: 35 minutes  ✱  Makes 6 servings

Per serving: 67 calories, 2 g protein, 8 g carbohydrates, 3 g total fat, 1 g saturated fat, 3 g fiber, 121 mg sodium

Remember that veggies are your allies when it comes to peeling off the pounds. With their fiber and high water content, they fill up your tummy.

# Summer Squash and Sweet Potato Pancakes

1 yellow squash

1 large sweet potato, peeled

2 scallions, white and green parts, minced

1 egg, lightly beaten

¼ teaspoon salt

⅛ teaspoon pepper

3 tablespoons olive oil, divided

Fat-free sour cream or applesauce (optional)

SLICE the squash lengthwise. Remove and discard the seeds. In a food processor or with a hand grater, coarsely grate the squash and potato. Remove to a medium bowl.

STIR in the scallions, egg, salt, and pepper.

HEAT 1½ tablespoons of the oil in a large nonstick skillet over medium-high heat. Working in 2 batches, drop heaping tablespoons of the mixture onto the skillet, gently flattening with the back of the spoon. Cook for about 2 minutes, or until the edges are golden. Flip and cook for about 1 minute, or until the bottom is golden. Adjust the heat if necessary to prevent burning. Remove to paper towels to drain.

REPEAT with the remaining 1½ tablespoons oil and zucchini mixture. There should be 24 pancakes. Serve with sour cream or applesauce (if using).

---

Total time: 20 minutes  ✽ Makes 8 servings (3 pancakes per serving)

Per serving: 85 calories, 2 g protein, 7 g carbohydrates, 6 g total fat, 1 g saturated fat, 1 g fiber, 98 mg sodium

You can make the pancakes up to 6 hours in advance. Cover and set aside at room temperature. Reheat on a baking sheet in a preheated 375°F oven for about 5 minutes, or until heated through.

# Asparagus and Sugar-Snap Toss

1½ teaspoons olive oil

1½ pounds asparagus, trimmed and cut into 1" pieces

1 tablespoon water

½ pound sugar snap peas, ends trimmed and strings removed

3 scallions, white and green parts, sliced

1½ teaspoons reduced-sodium soy sauce

1½ teaspoons honey

⅛ teaspoon salt

⅛ teaspoon pepper

**HEAT** the oil in a large skillet over medium heat. Add the asparagus and water. Cover and cook for 5 minutes. Stir in the peas, scallions, soy sauce, honey, salt, and pepper. Cover and cook for about 5 minutes, or until the vegetables are tender when pierced with a sharp knife.

---

Total time: 15 minutes ✱ Makes 8 servings

Per serving: 34 calories, 2 g protein, 5 g carbohydrates, 1 g total fat, 0 g saturated fat, 2 g fiber, 36 mg sodium

This medley of spring vegetables tastes as good at room temperature as it does hot.

[ **QUICK TIP: CUT PREP TIME**
Preheat the oven or put a pot of water on to boil as soon as you walk in the door. You'll be minutes closer to dinner. ]

# Roasted Broccoli with Orange

1 pound broccoli

2 tablespoons olive oil

2 cloves garlic, thinly sliced

2 teaspoons grated orange peel

½ teaspoon salt

2 tablespoons orange juice

⅛ teaspoon pepper

**PREHEAT** the oven to 425°F. Line a baking pan with foil.

**CUT** the broccoli tops into florets. Peel the stems, quarter lengthwise, and cut into 2" lengths. Combine the broccoli, oil, garlic, orange peel, and salt on the pan. Toss to mix.

**ROAST** for about 20 minutes, or until the stems are tender when pierced with a sharp knife.

**DRIZZLE** with the orange juice. Toss to coat. Sprinkle with the pepper.

---

Total time: 25 minutes ✱ Makes 4 servings

Per serving: 104 calories, 3 g protein, 9 g carbohydrates, 7 g total fat, 1 g saturated fat, 3 g fiber, 327 mg sodium

Roasting vegetables is one of the most foolproof ways to cook them. Just season on a baking sheet and let the oven's heat do all the rest.

> ## SUPERFOOD SPOTLIGHT: BROCCOLI
> Buy local broccoli during the colder months. It's at its freshest and most flavorful October through April.
>
> **Why:** Low in calories and high in vitamins A, C, and K, broccoli is easy to prepare and inexpensive. Many nutritionists think it helps prevent and may even fight cancer.
>
> **Try:** The green florets get the glory, but the stalks are just as tasty and nutritious. Many people even prefer them to the tops. Just peel for tenderness.

# Mesquite-Barbecued Corn

6 ears corn, halved

1½ tablespoons trans-free spread or butter, softened

3 scallions, white and light green parts, sliced

1 teaspoon mesquite seasoning

**PREHEAT** the grill or broiler to medium-high.

**PLACE** the corn in a single layer in an extra-heavy-duty foil cooking bag. Add the spread or butter, scallions, and seasoning. Close the bag. Fold tightly several times to seal. Place the bag in a broiler pan.

**GRILL** or broil, rotating occasionally and shaking the bag to distribute the seasonings, for about 25 minutes, or until sizzling.

--------------------------------------------------------------

Total time: 30 minutes ✱ Makes 6 servings

Per serving: 111 calories, 3 g protein, 20 g carbohydrates, 4 g total fat, 1 g saturated fat, 2 g fiber, 39 mg sodium

When you season corn on the cob with just a bit of butter and vivid mesquite seasoning, the fat and calories go way down.

# Savory Bread Stuffing

- 4 cups cubed reduced-sodium whole wheat bread
- 1 teaspoon olive oil
- 4 ribs celery, finely chopped
- 1 onion, chopped
- 2 teaspoons poultry seasoning
- ½ teaspoon dried thyme
- ¼ teaspoon pepper
- 1½ cups reduced-sodium chicken broth

**PREHEAT** the oven to 350°F. Coat a 12" × 8" baking dish with cooking spray. Coat a large baking sheet with cooking spray.

**SCATTER** the bread on the sheet and mist with cooking spray. Bake for 15 minutes, or until golden brown. Transfer to a large bowl.

**COAT** a nonstick skillet with cooking spray. Heat over medium-high heat. Cook the oil, celery, onion, seasoning, thyme, and pepper, stirring occasionally, for 5 minutes, or until the onion is soft.

**REMOVE** to the bowl with the bread. Add the broth and toss to mix. Spoon into the baking dish.

**BAKE** for 30 minutes, or until golden brown.

---

Total time: 55 minutes  ✳  Makes 8 servings

Per serving: 94 calories, 5 g protein, 15 g carbohydrates, 2 g total fat, 0 g saturated fat, 4 g fiber, 183 mg sodium

You don't have to wait for Thanksgiving to enjoy homemade stuffing as a side dish. We've eliminated the butter and moistened the bread with chicken broth to keep this version lean.

# Sesame Slaw

1½ tablespoons canola oil

2 teaspoons toasted sesame oil

⅛ teaspoon salt

Pinch of ground red pepper
(optional)

1 small head green cabbage,
shredded (1 pound)

½ small head red cabbage,
shredded (½ pound)

1 ounce baby spinach, shredded

8 snow peas, thinly sliced
diagonally

1 small onion, halved and thinly
sliced

IN a large bowl, whisk together the canola oil, sesame oil, salt, and pepper (if using). Add the green cabbage, red cabbage, spinach, snow peas, and onion. Toss.

COVER and refrigerate for at least 1 hour. Toss before serving.

-----

Total time: 1 hour 10 minutes ✱ Makes 4 servings

Per serving: 129 calories, 3 g protein, 14 g carbohydrates, 8 g total fat, 1 g saturated fat, 5 g fiber, 127 mg sodium

Foods that require chewing, like this sensational slaw, can help us slow the rate at which we eat.

# Curried Skillet Basmati Rice

1 small onion, chopped

½ teaspoon canola oil

1 clove garlic, minced

¾ cup basmati rice

½ teaspoon curry powder

1 can (14.5 ounces) reduced-sodium chicken broth

1 tablespoon sugar

½ teaspoon salt

**COAT** a large nonstick skillet with cooking spray. Heat over medium-high heat. Cook the onion, oil, and garlic, stirring, for 5 minutes, or until the onion is soft. Stir in the rice and curry powder. Cook and stir for 2 minutes, or until fragrant. Stir in the broth, sugar, and salt. Bring to a boil. Reduce the heat to low, cover, and cook for 20 minutes, or until the rice is tender.

Total time: 35 minutes ✱ Makes 4 servings

Per serving: 124 calories, 5 g protein, 22 g carbohydrates, 2 g total fat, 0 g saturated fat, 1 g fiber, 318 mg sodium

Indian cooks have a way with spicing grains and vegetables that keeps meals interesting.

## NUTRITION NEWS TO USE

Turmeric, a key ingredient in curry powder, packs more than just a mouthful of flavor. Its yellow pigment, curcumin, also helps ward off disease. Studies suggest that curcumin inhibits the growth of cancer, particularly colon cancer cells, and may even reduce the risk of Alzheimer's disease. Now a new study shows that it could also help prevent and treat a type of fatty liver disease that can lead to cirrhosis. To get some curry in a hurry, sprinkle curry powder on scrambled eggs—or add it to lentil soup, roasted sweet potatoes, or chicken salad for a dash of extra zing.

# Mushroom-Barley "Risotto"

- 2 teaspoons olive oil
- 4 ounces fresh mushrooms, chopped
- 3 scallions, all parts, sliced
- ½ teaspoon finely chopped fresh rosemary or crumbled dried
- ¼ teaspoon salt
- ⅛ teaspoon pepper
- ½ cup instant barley
- ¾ cup reduced-sodium chicken broth
- 2 teaspoons balsamic vinegar

**COAT** a skillet with cooking spray. Swirl the oil in the pan and heat over medium-high heat. Stir in the mushrooms, scallions, rosemary, salt, and pepper. Cook and stir for 2 minutes, or until the mushrooms give off liquid.

**ADD** the barley. Cook and stir for 2 minutes, or until the barley is coated with the seasonings. Stir in the broth and bring to a boil.

**REDUCE** the heat to medium-low, cover, and cook for about 10 minutes, or until the barley is tender. Remove and let stand, covered, for a few minutes, or until all of the liquid is absorbed. Stir in the vinegar.

---

Total time: 25 minutes  ✱  Makes 4 servings

Per serving: 115 calories, 4 g protein, 19 g carbohydrates, 3 g total fat, 1 g saturated fat, 4 g fiber, 177 mg sodium

The pairing of mushrooms and barley is a classic for soup. Now try it in this risotto-style grain dish. Baby portobello mushrooms—sometimes labeled as "baby bellas"—are especially full-bodied, but any type of fresh mushroom can be used here.

# Couscous Salad with Parmesan Dressing

1½ cups reduced-sodium chicken broth or water

¾ cup whole grain couscous

2 tablespoons extra virgin olive oil

1 tablespoon white wine vinegar

1 tablespoon grated Parmesan cheese

Pinch of salt

Pinch of black pepper

1 small tomato, chopped

1 cucumber, chopped

¼ red bell pepper, chopped

1 tablespoon chopped fresh mint

BRING the broth or water to a boil in a large saucepan over high heat. Stir in the couscous and remove from the heat. Cover and let stand for 5 minutes.

IN a large bowl, whisk together the oil, vinegar, cheese, salt, and black pepper. Stir in the tomato, cucumber, bell pepper, and mint. With a fork, scrape the couscous into the bowl. Toss to mix.

------------------------------------------------

Total time: 10 minutes ✸ Makes 4 servings

Per serving: 170 calories, 5 g protein, 21 g carbohydrates, 8 g total fat, 1 g saturated fat, 4 g fiber, 239 mg sodium

Whole grain couscous is wonderful to keep on hand because it reconstitutes in no time. Instead of the boxed couscous with high-sodium seasonings, look for whole grain couscous in the bulk section of the supermarket.

# Asian Pear and Pecan Tossed Salad

¼ cup part-skim ricotta cheese

1 tablespoon grated Romano cheese

3 tablespoons extra virgin olive oil

1 tablespoon red wine vinegar

⅛ teaspoon salt

⅛ teaspoon pepper

1 head green leaf lettuce (¾ pound), torn into bite-size pieces

1 Asian pear, thinly sliced

¼ cup chopped pecans, toasted (see note page 98)

IN a small bowl, stir together the ricotta and Romano.

IN a large bowl, whisk together the oil, vinegar, salt, and pepper. Add the lettuce and pear. Toss to coat with the dressing. Divide among 4 plates. Sprinkle with the pecans and top with small dollops of the cheese mixture.

--------------------------------------------------

Total time: 10 minutes  ✳  Makes 4 servings

Per serving: 149 calories, 4 g protein, 6 g carbohydrates, 13 g total fat, 3 g saturated fat, 1 g fiber, 141 mg sodium

Asian pears combine the crispness of apples with the sweet taste of pears. In this dish, the cheese blend sets off the fruit's unique qualities.

# Zucchini and Bean Salad

2 tablespoons extra virgin olive oil

1 tablespoon lemon juice

1 tablespoon finely chopped fresh parsley

1 small clove garlic, crushed

¾ teaspoon dried oregano

Pinch of salt

2 zucchini, unpeeled, chopped

1 can (15 ounces) cannellini beans, rinsed and drained

1 small red bell pepper, finely chopped

1 small tomato, finely chopped

1 tablespoon finely chopped red onion

Red-pepper flakes (optional)

IN a large mixing bowl, whisk together the oil, lemon juice, parsley, garlic, oregano, and salt. Add the zucchini, beans, bell pepper, tomato, and onion. Toss to coat with the dressing. Sprinkle with red-pepper flakes, if desired.

--------------------------------------

Total time: 10 minutes ✽ Makes 4 servings

Per serving: 155 calories, 6 g protein, 17 g carbohydrates, 7 g total fat, 1 g saturated fat, 5 g fiber, 241 mg sodium

Cannellini are white kidney beans that are particularly enjoyed in northern Italian cooking. Great Northern beans work just as well in this dish.

# Potato Salad with Warm Onion Dressing

2 pounds red potatoes, cut into large chunks

1 tablespoon canola oil

1 red onion, chopped

1 clove garlic, chopped

¼ cup chopped fresh parsley

3 tablespoons cider vinegar

3 tablespoons apple juice

1 tablespoon stone-ground mustard

⅛ teaspoon salt

**PLACE** a steamer basket in a saucepan with ½" water over high heat. Place the potatoes in the steamer. Cover and bring to a boil. Reduce the heat to medium and cook for 20 minutes, or until tender. Rinse briefly under cold running water, then drain and pat dry. Remove to a large serving bowl.

**MEANWHILE,** heat the oil in a medium nonstick skillet over medium heat. Cook the onion and garlic, stirring occasionally, for 8 minutes, or until the onion is very soft.

**STIR** in the parsley, vinegar, apple juice, mustard, and salt. Cook for 2 minutes, or until heated through. Pour over the potatoes. Toss to coat well.

**LET** stand for 15 minutes to allow the flavors to blend.

Total time: 40 minutes  ✳  Makes 6 servings

Per serving: 142 calories, 3 g protein, 28 g carbohydrates, 3 g total fat, 0 g saturated fat, 3 g fiber, 92 mg sodium

Salads don't have to be exclusively summertime fare. This hearty plate is substantial enough to accompany baked pork chops when the cold winds blow.

# Roasted Vegetable Salad

| | |
|---|---|
| 1½ | pounds small red potatoes, quartered |
| ¾ | pound green beans, cut into 1" pieces |
| 2 | red bell peppers, thinly sliced |
| 1 | red onion, thinly sliced crosswise and separated into rings |
| ½ | cup reduced-sodium chicken broth |
| 2 | cloves garlic |
| 2 | tablespoons red wine vinegar |
| 1½ | tablespoons olive oil |
| 1 | teaspoon dried rosemary, crushed |
| ¼ | teaspoon black pepper |
| 8 | kalamata olives, pitted and sliced |
| 2 | tablespoons lemon juice |

**PREHEAT** the oven to 425°F. Coat a 13" × 9" baking dish with cooking spray. Add the potatoes, beans, bell peppers, onion, broth, and garlic. Roast, stirring occasionally, for about 25 minutes, or until the vegetables are tender.

**REMOVE** the garlic to a large bowl and mash with the back of a spoon. Whisk in the vinegar, oil, rosemary, and black pepper. Add the olives, lemon juice, and the roasted vegetables. Toss to mix well.

Total time: 30 minutes  ✳  Makes 4 servings

Per serving: 225 calories, 5 g protein, 37 g carbohydrates, 7 g total fat, 1 g saturated fat, 7 g fiber, 196 mg sodium

You can prepare this salad ahead of time when you're using the oven for a different recipe. Cool and refrigerate in a tightly covered container. Bring to room temperature, and toss with the lemon juice just before serving.

# Green Bean–Tomato Salad with Cracked Mustard Seeds

2 teaspoons canola oil

1 small clove garlic, minced

½ teaspoon mustard seeds, cracked

1 tablespoon white wine vinegar

⅛ teaspoon salt

1 pound green beans

12 cherry tomatoes, halved

IN a small microwaveable dish, combine the oil, garlic, and mustard seeds. Cover with plastic wrap, leaving a small air vent. Microwave on high power for 1 minute, or until sizzling. Remove and let stand to cool. Remove the plastic and whisk in the vinegar and salt.

BRING a saucepan of water to a boil. Cook the beans for about 2 minutes, or until tender. Drain and rinse with cold running water. Drain and pat dry.

REMOVE the beans to a mixing bowl. Add the tomatoes and the reserved oil mixture. Toss to coat with the dressing.

Total time: 10 minutes  ✱  Makes 4 servings

Per serving: 67 calories, 3 g protein, 10 g carbohydrates, 3 g total fat, 0 g saturated fat, 4 g fiber, 83 mg sodium

Rely on calorie "freebie" seasonings, like the mustard seeds, garlic, and vinegar used here, to keep your meals appetizing without piling on the calories.

# Cucumber Salad with Dill

2 large cucumbers, sliced

⅔ cup fat-free sour cream

½ small apple, chopped

3 radishes, thinly sliced

2 scallions, all parts, thinly sliced

1 teaspoon chopped fresh dill

½ teaspoon salt

½ teaspoon pepper

IN a large bowl, toss together the cucumbers, sour cream, apple, radishes, scallions, dill, salt, and pepper. Cover and refrigerate for 30 minutes to allow the flavors to blend.

---

Total time: 40 minutes  ✳  Makes 4 servings

Per serving: 86 calories, 4 g protein, 18 g carbohydrates, 0 g total fat, 0 g saturated fat, 2 g fiber, 330 mg sodium

This zesty side dish complements the smoky undertones of grilled chicken or pork.

# Creamy Potato Salad with Corn and Peas

5 potatoes, cubed

¾ cup low-fat sour cream

¼ cup fat-free mayonnaise

¼ cup finely chopped fresh parsley

2 tablespoons fresh basil, loosely torn

½ teaspoon black pepper

½ cup fresh or frozen and thawed corn kernels

½ cup frozen and thawed baby peas

¼ cup chopped red bell peppers or jarred roasted red peppers

BRING a large pot of water to a boil over medium-high heat. Cook the potatoes for 10 minutes, or until tender. Drain in a colander. Pat dry.

IN a large bowl, stir together the sour cream, mayonnaise, parsley, basil, and black pepper. Stir in the corn, peas, red pepper, and potatoes. Toss well to coat. Cover and refrigerate for 20 minutes, or until chilled.

----

Total time: 40 minutes ✳ Makes 5 servings

Per serving: 191 calories, 5 g protein, 36 g carbohydrates, 4 g total fat, 2 g saturated fat, 3 g fiber, 176 mg sodium

This family-friendly dish becomes even tastier—and more healthful—with the addition of colorful corn, peas, and bell peppers.

# desserts

# Peppermint Patty Cake

### Cake

- 1½ cups granulated sugar, divided
- 1 cup all-purpose flour
- ¾ cup unsweetened cocoa powder
- 2 teaspoons baking powder
- 1 teaspoon baking soda
- ⅛ teaspoon salt
- 6 egg whites
- ⅔ cup prune puree
- ½ cup water
- ⅓ cup buttermilk
- 2 egg yolks
- 2 tablespoons canola oil
- 2 teaspoons instant coffee powder
- ¼ teaspoon peppermint extract

### Frosting

- 1 cup confectioners' sugar
- 2 tablespoons fat-free milk
- ⅛ teaspoon peppermint extract
- 2 cups fat-free nondairy whipped topping

To make the cake:

PREHEAT the oven to 350°F. Coat a 13" × 9" baking dish with cooking spray. Line with waxed paper. Coat with cooking spray.

IN a medium bowl, stir together 1 cup of the granulated sugar, the flour, cocoa, baking powder, baking soda, and salt.

PLACE the egg whites in a large bowl. With an electric mixer on medium speed, beat for 1 minute, or until soft peaks form. Beat, while gradually adding the remaining ½ cup granulated sugar, for about 2 minutes, or until stiff peaks form.

IN a large bowl, whisk together the prune puree, water, buttermilk, egg yolks, oil, coffee powder, and peppermint extract. Stir in the flour mixture just until no flour is visible. Fold in the beaten egg whites. Pour into the baking dish.

BAKE for 30 to 35 minutes, or until a wooden pick inserted in the center comes out clean. Cool in the pan on a rack.

To make the frosting:

IN a medium bowl, whisk together the confectioners' sugar, milk, and peppermint extract until smooth. Fold in the whipped topping. Spread over the cake. Refrigerate for 2 hours.

Total time: 2 hours 40 minutes ✱ Makes 12 servings

Per serving: 281 calories, 5 g protein, 59 g carbohydrates, 4 g total fat, 1 g saturated fat, 3 g fiber, 259 mg sodium

## [ QUICK TIP: JAVA BEFORE THE GYM ]

Drink a cup of coffee an hour before you exercise: Caffeine can help increase your endurance and delay fatigue.

# Chocolate Spice Cake

1 cup all-purpose flour

½ cup sugar

3 tablespoons unsweetened cocoa powder

1 teaspoon ground cinnamon

1 teaspoon baking soda

¼ teaspoon salt

2 eggs, separated

1 cup fat-free plain yogurt

2 tablespoons trans-free spread or butter, melted

1 teaspoon vanilla extract

Fat-free whipped cream (optional)

PREHEAT the oven to 350°F. Coat an 8" × 8" baking pan with cooking spray.

IN a large bowl, stir together the flour, sugar, cocoa, cinnamon, baking soda, and salt.

IN a mixing bowl, with an electric mixer on medium speed, beat the egg whites for 1 minute, or until frothy. Beat on high speed for 2 minutes, or until stiff peaks form.

IN a medium bowl, whisk together the yogurt, spread or butter, vanilla, and egg yolks. Stir into the flour mixture. Fold in the egg whites. Pour into the baking pan.

BAKE for about 35 minutes, or until a wooden pick inserted in the center comes out clean. Cool in the pan on a rack.

SERVE with whipped cream (if using).

Total time: 45 minutes ✱ Makes 8 servings

Per serving: 161 calories, 5 g protein, 28 g carbohydrates, 4 g total fat, 2 g saturated fat, 1 g fiber, 279 mg sodium

## QUICK TIP: GIVE YOUR APPETITE A REST

It takes only 1 night of sleep deprivation to increase levels of ghrelin (the hormone that triggers hunger) and decrease levels of leptin (which suppresses hunger). As a result, your body thinks you're starving, which spikes cravings for high-fat and high-calorie foods, says Ann E. Rogers, RN, PhD, associate professor at the University of Pennsylvania School of Nursing.

# Apricot-Blueberry Bundt Cake

1½ cups whole grain pastry flour

1½ cups all-purpose flour

1½ cups granulated sugar

½ cup ground flaxseed

1 tablespoon baking powder

1 teaspoon baking soda

¼ teaspoon salt

1⅓ cups buttermilk

6 tablespoons canola oil

4 eggs

1 teaspoon vanilla extract

2 cups fresh or frozen and thawed blueberries

4 apricots, chopped

1 cup confectioners' sugar

6 teaspoons fresh lemon juice

**PREHEAT** the oven to 350°F. Coat a 12-cup tube or Bundt pan with cooking spray and sprinkle lightly with flour to coat.

**IN** a large bowl, stir together the whole grain flour, all-purpose flour, sugar, flaxseed, baking powder, baking soda, and salt.

**IN** another bowl, with an electric mixer on low speed, beat together the buttermilk, oil, eggs, and vanilla. Stir into the flour mixture and beat with an electric mixer on medium speed for about 1 minute, or until well combined. Fold in the blueberries and apricots. Pour into the baking pan.

**BAKE** for about 45 minutes, or until a wooden pick inserted in the center comes out clean. Cool in the pan on a rack for 15 minutes. Carefully remove from the pan and cool on the rack for 30 minutes.

**TRANSFER** the cake to a serving platter. In a small bowl, whisk together the confectioners' sugar and lemon juice. Drizzle over the top of the cake and let stand for 5 minutes to set.

------------------------------------------------------------

Total time: 1 hour 45 minutes ✱ Makes 24 servings

Per serving: 199 calories, 4 g protein, 34 g carbohydrates, 6 g total fat, 1 g saturated fat, 2 g fiber, 154 mg sodium

Bundt cakes freeze very well. Wrap cooled single servings in plastic wrap and freeze for convenient brown-bag lunches or an "instant" dessert for unexpected guests.

# Dark Chocolate Chiffon Cake

Cake

- 5 egg whites
- ½ teaspoon cream of tartar
- 1 package (18.25 ounces) devil's food cake mix
- ¾ cup water
- ½ cup canola oil
- 3 egg yolks
- 1 tablespoon instant coffee powder
- 1 teaspoon vanilla extract

Frosting

- 3 tablespoons trans-free spread or butter, at room temperature
- 3 tablespoons unsweetened cocoa powder
- 1 cup confectioners' sugar
- 2 tablespoons whole milk
- 1 teaspoon vanilla extract

To make the cake:

PREHEAT the oven to 325°F.

IN a medium bowl, combine the egg whites and cream of tartar. Beat with an electric mixer on high speed for about 3 minutes, or until stiff peaks form.

IN a large bowl, combine the cake mix, water, oil, egg yolks, coffee powder, and vanilla. With the unwashed beaters, blend on low speed for 1 minute. Scrape the sides of the bowl with a spatula. Increase the mixer speed to medium and beat for 2 minutes, or until smooth. Fold in the egg whites. Pour into a 10" tube pan, smoothing the top with the spatula.

BAKE for about 50 minutes, or until a wooden pick inserted in the center comes out clean. Remove and set the pan upside down over the neck of a glass bottle to cool for 1 hour. Remove the pan from the bottle. Run a long, sharp knife around the outer and inner edges of the cake and invert it onto a rack, then invert it again onto a serving platter.

To make the frosting:

IN a medium bowl, combine the spread or butter and cocoa. Blend with an electric mixer on low speed for 30 seconds. Add the sugar, milk, and vanilla. Increase the mixer speed to medium and beat for 1 minute, or until fluffy. Spread over the top and sides of the cake.

----

Total time: 2 hours  ✱  Makes 16 servings

Per serving: 268 calories, 4 g protein, 33 g carbohydrates, 14 g total fat, 3 g saturated fat, 1 g fiber, 277 mg sodium

This cake makes a wonderful dish to share with a group of friends for a potluck.

# Pear-Cranberry Upside-Down Cake

Topping

- 3 tablespoons trans-free spread or butter
- ¼ cup packed light brown sugar
- 1 tablespoon maple syrup
- 3 Bartlett or Anjou pears
- ½ cup fresh cranberries

Cake

- ½ cup packed light brown sugar
- 5 tablespoons trans-free spread or butter, melted
- ½ cup orange juice
- ¼ cup pure maple syrup
- 2 eggs
- 1 teaspoon vanilla extract
- 1½ cups all-purpose flour
- 1½ teaspoons baking powder
- 2½ teaspoons pumpkin pie spice
- ¼ teaspoon salt

To make the topping:

**PREHEAT** the oven to 375°F.

**IN** a 9" round heatproof baking pan, stir together the spread or butter, sugar, and syrup. Cook over medium heat for about 90 seconds, or until the mixture starts to bubble. Remove to a trivet.

**HALVE** the pears and cut each half lengthwise into 6 slices. Arrange in a circle in the pan, overlapping slightly, with the narrow necks toward the center. Pile the cranberries in the center. Place a few cranberries around the outside edge of the pan between the pear slices.

**BAKE** for 15 minutes, or until the pears are tender.

To make the cake:

**MEANWHILE,** in a large bowl, whisk together the sugar, spread or butter, orange juice, syrup, eggs, and vanilla. Stir in the flour, baking powder, spice, and salt until blended. Pour into the pan.

**BAKE** for about 30 minutes, or until a tester inserted in the center comes out clean. Cool in the pan on a rack for about 3 minutes, then run a knife between the cake and the sides of the pan. Cover the pan with a flat serving plate. With oven mitts, invert the cake onto the platter. Cool for about 5 minutes.

---

Total time: 1 hour 10 minutes ✻ Makes 12 servings

Per serving: 243 calories, 3 g protein, 40 g carbohydrates, 9 g total fat, 5 g saturated fat, 2 g fiber, 119 mg sodium

## SUPERFOOD SPOTLIGHT: CRANBERRIES

With their cheery hue and tart taste, cranberries wake up muffins, add zing to pork, and make a seriously healthy sandwich spread. Cranberries also, famously, help maintain urinary tract health and are a good source of vitamin C and fiber. Fresh, they last 2 to 4 weeks in the fridge and up to a year in the freezer (store in their original packaging or a resealable plastic bag). Grab them October through December, when they're available.

# Lemon Pound Cake

2¼ cups all-purpose flour

1¼ cups sugar

2 teaspoons baking powder

¼ teaspoon baking soda

¼ teaspoon salt

1 cup fat-free sour cream

½ cup trans-free spread or butter, at room temperature

2 egg whites

¼ cup fat-free milk

1½ teaspoons lemon extract

1 teaspoon grated lemon peel

PREHEAT the oven to 350°F. Coat a 9" × 5" nonstick loaf pan with cooking spray and dust lightly with flour.

IN a large bowl, stir together the flour, sugar, baking powder, baking soda, and salt.

IN a large bowl, combine the sour cream, spread or butter, egg whites, milk, lemon extract, and lemon peel. With an electric mixer on low speed, beat for 1 minute. Add the flour mixture. Beat on low speed for 1 minute. Beat at medium speed for 2 minutes, scraping the sides of the bowl once or twice, or until light and fluffy. Pour into the baking pan and smooth the top.

BAKE for about 60 minutes, or until a wooden pick inserted in the center comes out clean. Cool in the pan on a rack for 10 minutes. Turn out onto the rack and cool completely.

---

Total time: 2 hours 30 minutes  ✽  Makes 16 servings

Per serving: 196 calories, 3 g protein, 33 g carbohydrates, 6 g total fat, 4 g saturated fat, 0 g fiber, 187 mg sodium

Lemon lovers, rejoice: This moist cake has fewer than 200 calories per serving.

# Sweet Potato Cake with Orange Glaze

2 large sweet potatoes, halved

3 cups all-purpose flour

1 cup packed light brown sugar

1 tablespoon baking powder

1 teaspoon baking soda

½ teaspoon salt

¼ cup golden or dark raisins

¼ cup canola oil

¼ cup buttermilk

2 egg yolks

4 tablespoons orange juice, divided

3 egg whites

¼ cup confectioners' sugar

½ teaspoon grated orange peel

PREHEAT the oven to 400°F. Place the potatoes on a baking sheet.

BAKE for 40 minutes, or until very soft when pierced with a sharp knife. Cool, peel, and mash the potatoes. Set aside 2 cups. Reserve any remaining mashed potatoes for another recipe.

REDUCE the oven temperature to 350°F. Coat a 9" × 5" loaf pan with cooking spray. Lightly dust the pan with flour, shaking off any excess.

IN a large bowl, stir together the flour, brown sugar, baking powder, baking soda, and salt. Stir in the raisins.

IN a medium bowl, whisk together the oil, buttermilk, egg yolks, potatoes, and 2 tablespoons of the orange juice until smooth. Stir into the dry ingredients until no flour is visible.

IN a medium bowl, beat the egg whites with an electric beater on medium speed for about 2 minutes, or until soft peaks form. Fold into the batter. Pour into the loaf pan.

BAKE for 1 hour to 1 hour 10 minutes, or until lightly browned and a wooden pick inserted in the center comes out clean. Cool in the pan on a rack.

UNMOLD the cake onto a platter. In a small bowl, whisk together the confectioners' sugar, orange peel, and the remaining 2 tablespoons orange juice. Drizzle over the cake.

Total time: 2 hours 30 minutes ✳ Makes 16 servings

Per serving: 236 calories, 4 g protein, 46 g carbohydrates, 4 g total fat, 1 g saturated fat, 2 g fiber, 363 mg sodium

Sweet potatoes are wonders! They're low in calories, high in fiber, and packed with vitamins and minerals. The *Nutrition Action Healthletter* once rated the sweet potato the number one healthiest vegetable.

# Cappuccino Pudding Cake

¾ cup packed dark brown sugar

¾ cup granulated sugar, divided

¼ cup + 2 tablespoons unsweetened cocoa powder, divided

1 teaspoon + 2 tablespoons instant espresso powder, divided

⅜ teaspoon salt, divided

1 cup whole grain pastry flour

¼ cup nonfat dry milk

2 teaspoons baking powder

¼ teaspoon ground cinnamon

½ cup 1% milk

¼ cup canola oil

1 teaspoon vanilla extract

1¾ cups very hot water

**PREHEAT** the oven to 350°F. In a small bowl, stir together the brown sugar, ¼ cup of the granulated sugar, ¼ cup of the cocoa, 1 teaspoon of the espresso powder, and ⅛ teaspoon of the salt. Set aside.

**IN** a medium bowl, stir together the flour, dry milk, baking powder, cinnamon, and the remaining ½ cup granulated sugar, 2 tablespoons cocoa, 2 tablespoons espresso powder, and ¼ teaspoon salt.

**IN** a small bowl, whisk together the 1% milk, oil, and vanilla. Stir into the flour mixture until no white is visible. Pour into a 9" × 9" baking pan. Spread the top evenly. Sprinkle with the reserved brown sugar mixture. Carefully pour the hot water over the top.

**BAKE** for 40 minutes, or until the top is set and the mixture is bubbling. Serve warm or at room temperature.

-------------------------------------------------------------

Total time: 1 hour 15 minutes ✳ Makes 10 servings

Per serving: 295 calories, 4 g protein, 55 g carbohydrates, 8 g total fat, 2 g saturated fat, 3 g fiber, 259 mg sodium

A layer of yummy pudding rises to the top as this cake bakes. Turn the cake onto a platter to serve.

# Cherry Pudding Cake

2 cups frozen and thawed dark sweet cherries

1 cup fat-free plain yogurt

½ cup part-skim ricotta cheese

¼ cup all-purpose flour

¼ cup granulated sugar

2 eggs

¼ teaspoon ground nutmeg

¼ cup raisins

2 tablespoons packed light brown sugar

PREHEAT the oven to 400°F. Coat a 12" quiche dish with cooking spray. Scatter the cherries into the dish.

IN a blender or food processor, combine the yogurt, ricotta, flour, granulated sugar, eggs, and nutmeg. Blend or process until smooth. Pour over the cherries and sprinkle with the raisins.

BAKE for 15 to 18 minutes, or until the cake begins to set. Sprinkle with the brown sugar. Bake for 10 minutes, or until the cake is firm and golden brown. Serve warm.

---

Total time: 25 minutes   ✱   Makes 6 servings

Per serving: 191 calories, 7 g protein, 35 g carbohydrates, 4 g total fat, 2 g saturated fat, 1 g fiber, 74 mg sodium

Dense, moist, and packed with sweet fruit, this calorie-trimmed dessert is sure to satisfy.

> ## QUICK TIP: THE STAY-SLIM RESTAURANT STRATEGY
> What your friends order when you eat out could make you gain weight—even if they're thin. In a new study, normal-weight women were more likely to adjust their eating to mimic a thin woman's than an obese woman's. And whether the svelte dining partner overate or underate, the study participant did the same. So when you go out with the gang, order first. That way, you'll be less likely to be influenced by others, researchers say.

# Rainbow Sorbet Angel Cake

1 prepared angel food cake (10 ounces)

1 pint strawberry or raspberry sorbet, soft enough to scoop

½ pint mango or peach sorbet, soft enough to scoop

½ cup confectioners' sugar

3 tablespoons frozen limeade concentrate

**WITH** a serrated knife, cut the cake into 3 equal layers. Place the bottom layer, cut side up, on a freezerproof serving plate. Spread on the strawberry or raspberry sorbet in an even layer. Top with the second cake layer. Spread the mango or peach sorbet in an even layer. Top with the last cake layer. With a spatula, smooth any sorbet that oozes out on the sides of the cake, like frosting. Cover with plastic wrap. Freeze for several hours, or until the sorbet is solid.

**REMOVE** and let stand at room temperature for 20 minutes. In a small bowl, whisk together the sugar and limeade concentrate. Drizzle over the cake, allowing it to run down the sides. Cut with a serrated knife.

---

Total time: 2 hours 10 minutes ✱ Makes 12 servings

Per serving: 152 calories, 1 g protein, 38 g carbohydrates, 0 g total fat, 0 g saturated fat, 1 g fiber, 182 mg sodium

This dessert requires very little work but makes a stunning presentation.

# Pecan Strawberry Shortcake

5 egg whites, at room temperature

⅛ teaspoon salt

¼ cup confectioners' sugar

¼ teaspoon cream of tartar

1 teaspoon grated lime peel

1 teaspoon rum extract

2 tablespoons finely ground pecans

1 cup low-fat frozen whipped topping, thawed

1 pint strawberries, sliced

Mint sprigs (optional)

**PREHEAT** the oven to 275°F. Cover a baking sheet with parchment paper and coat with cooking spray.

**IN** a large bowl, combine the egg whites and salt. Beat with an electric mixer on high speed for 1 minute, or until frothy. Gradually sprinkle in the confectioners' sugar and cream of tartar, beating well after each addition. Add the lime peel and rum extract. Beat for about 2 minutes, or until stiff peaks form. Fold in the pecans.

**DOLLOP** the mixture into a 7" circle on the prepared pan. Bake for about 1 hour, or until golden.

**TURN** off the oven and let stand with the door open for about 30 minutes, or until cool. Remove from the parchment to a serving plate. Top with the whipped topping, strawberries, and mint (if using).

---

Total time: 1 hour 40 minutes ❋ Makes 4 servings

Per serving: 145 calories, 6 g protein, 19 g carbohydrates, 5 g total fat, 2 g saturated fat, 2 g fiber, 156 mg sodium

Depending upon the season, serve these tender nut-meringue shortcakes with raspberries, blackberries, or blueberries. Or include some of each.

## SUPERFOOD SPOTLIGHT: STRAWBERRIES

Luscious, heavenly scented, and red all the way through—these are the signs of a strawberry picked at its peak. And what you see—and smell—is what you get: This fruit doesn't continue to ripen after harvest. Choose deeply colored berries and avoid mushy ones. Consider buying organic because strawberries retain a high level of pesticide residue. Chill whole, unwashed berries in a single layer, loosely covered. Just before using, rinse gently in a bowl of cold water (don't run them under the tap) and dry on paper towels (wet berries spoil faster). Then enjoy! Strawberries are rich in antioxidants and, ounce for ounce, have more vitamin C than oranges.

# Gingerbread with Honey-Lemon Sauce

Gingerbread

2¼ cups all-purpose flour

2 teaspoons baking soda

1 tablespoon ground ginger

½ teaspoon ground cloves

1 cup molasses

1 cup buttermilk

½ cup packed light brown sugar

⅓ cup unsweetened applesauce

¼ cup canola oil

2 eggs

Sauce

1 cup fat-free plain yogurt

2 tablespoons honey

1 teaspoon grated lemon peel

To make the gingerbread:

**PREHEAT** the oven to 350°F. Coat a 10" tube pan with cooking spray. Dust with flour and shake out any excess.

**IN** a medium bowl, combine the 2¼ cups flour, baking soda, ginger, and cloves.

**IN** a large bowl, stir together the molasses, buttermilk, sugar, applesauce, oil, and eggs.

**STIR** in the dry ingredients until no flour is visible. Pour into the tube pan.

**BAKE** for about 35 minutes, or until a wooden pick inserted in the center comes out clean. Cool in the pan on a rack.

To make the sauce:

**IN** a small bowl, whisk together the yogurt, honey, and lemon peel. Spoon the sauce over each serving or next to it.

----

Total time: 1 hour 30 minutes  ✽  Makes 12 servings

Per serving: 247 calories, 4 g protein, 46 g carbohydrates, 6 g total fat, 1 g saturated fat, 1 g fiber, 269 mg sodium

This old-fashioned cake comes alive with a sprightly citrus sauce.

# Pineapple Upside-Down Cupcakes

- ½ cup packed light brown sugar
- 9 tablespoons trans-free spread or butter, softened, divided
- 3 pineapple rings, quartered
- 1 cup all-purpose flour
- ¼ cup nonfat dry milk
- 1 teaspoon baking powder
- ¼ teaspoon baking soda
- ¼ teaspoon salt
- ½ cup granulated sugar
- ½ cup fat-free lemon-flavored yogurt
- ¼ cup water
- 1 egg
- ¼ teaspoon lemon extract

**PREHEAT** the oven to 350°F. Coat a 12-cup nonstick muffin pan with cooking spray.

**DIVIDE** the brown sugar, 4 tablespoons of the spread or butter, and the pineapple among the cups.

**IN** a medium bowl, stir together the flour, dry milk, baking powder, baking soda, and salt.

**IN** a large bowl, beat the remaining 5 tablespoons spread or butter with an electric mixer on low speed until creamy. Beat while adding the granulated sugar until fluffy. Beat in the yogurt, water, egg, and lemon extract. Stir in the dry ingredients until no flour is visible.

**DIVIDE** the batter among the cups.

**BAKE** for 25 minutes, or until the cupcakes are browned and spring back when pressed lightly with a finger. Cool in the pan on a rack for 5 minutes. Turn the cupcakes onto a serving tray. Set aside to cool.

------------------------------------------

Total time: 1 hour ✳ Makes 12

Per serving: 185 calories, 3 g protein, 28 g carbohydrates, 7 g total fat, 2 g saturated fat, 1 g fiber, 199 mg sodium

Downsizing this classic American baked good is a clever tactic to ensure portion control.

## SUPERFOOD SPOTLIGHT: PINEAPPLE

Luscious, tart-sweet pineapple is full of nutrients as well as flavor. In addition to supplying vitamin C, a cup contains your daily quota of manganese, a trace mineral that promotes bone health. Though available all year round, this tropical fruit is at its peak from March through June. Go ahead and cut it into chunks and store in the fridge or buy it precut for convenience—the fruit retains its nutritional punch for up to a week.

# Devil's Food and Cheesecake Cupcakes

1 cup all-purpose flour

⅓ cup unsweetened cocoa powder

¾ teaspoon baking soda

Dash of salt

3 tablespoons canola oil

2 tablespoons trans-free spread or butter, at room temperature

1 ounce unsweetened chocolate, chopped

⅔ cup + 3 tablespoons sugar

2 teaspoons vanilla extract, divided

1 egg, beaten

⅓ cup buttermilk

⅓ cup hot water

¼ cup (2 ounces) reduced-fat cream cheese, at room temperature

¼ cup (2 ounces) fat-free cream cheese, at room temperature

PREHEAT the oven to 350°F. Line a 12-cup muffin pan with paper liners. Lightly coat the liners with cooking spray.

IN a small bowl, stir together the flour, cocoa, baking soda, and salt. Set aside.

IN a large microwaveable bowl, combine the oil, spread or butter, and chocolate. Microwave on high power for 1 minute, or until hot. Stir in ⅔ cup of the sugar and 1 teaspoon of the vanilla. Add 3 tablespoons of the egg. Beat until smooth. Gradually add the reserved dry ingredients alternately with the buttermilk and water. Mix until blended. Spoon 1 heaping tablespoon of batter into each cup. Set aside the remaining batter.

IN a medium bowl, beat together the cream cheeses until very smooth. Add the remaining 3 tablespoons sugar, beaten egg, and 1 teaspoon vanilla. Stir slowly to combine, then beat until very smooth. Divide the batter among the cups. Divide the remaining chocolate batter among the cups. Swirl with the back of a spoon to even the tops.

BAKE for about 20 minutes, or until a cupcake springs back when pressed lightly with a finger. Cool in the pan on a rack.

------

Total time: 1 hour  ✳  Makes 12

Per serving: 182 calories, 4 g protein, 26 g carbohydrates, 8 g total fat, 2 g saturated fat, 2 g fiber, 161 mg sodium

Talk about a win-win: Chocolate cake and cheesecake unite in these delectable little morsels.

# Triple Chocolate Cheesecake

1 package (9 ounces) chocolate wafer cookies

¼ cup trans-free spread or butter, melted

7 ounces semisweet chocolate chips

2 packages (8 ounces each) fat-free cream cheese, at room temperature

1 package (8 ounces) reduced-fat cream cheese, at room temperature

¾ cup sugar

¼ cup unsweetened cocoa powder

1½ teaspoons vanilla extract

½ teaspoon salt

3 eggs

**PREHEAT** the oven to 325°F. Coat a nonstick 9" round springform pan with cooking spray. Set on a sheet of heavy-duty foil. Wrap the foil up the sides of the pan. Set in a flat roasting pan.

**GRIND** the wafers in a food processor to form fine crumbs. Set aside ¼ cup. With the processor running, add the spread or butter. Press the mixture onto the bottom of the prepared pan.

**BAKE** for about 12 minutes, or until set  Set aside.

**MEANWHILE,** bring a kettle of water to a boil. Place the chips in a microwaveable bowl and microwave on high power for about 90 seconds, or until melted.

**IN** a mixing bowl, combine the cream cheeses. Beat with an electric mixer on medium speed for about 1 minute, or until blended. Add the sugar, cocoa, vanilla, and salt. Beat for about 1 minute, or until fluffy. Beat in the eggs, one at a time, on low speed until blended. Add the chocolate. Beat for 30 seconds to blend. Pour into the springform pan. Place in the oven and carefully pour boiling water into the roasting pan to reach halfway up the sides of the cheesecake pan.

**BAKE** for about 40 minutes, or until the center is almost set but still a bit jiggly. Turn off the heat and crack the oven door open with the handle of a wooden spoon. Allow to cool in the oven for 1 hour.

**REMOVE** from the oven. Transfer to a rack. Remove the foil. Allow to cool to room temperature. Run a knife between the pan and the sides of the cake. Refrigerate for at least 8 hours.

**SPRINKLE** the reserved cookie crumbs on top.

----

Total time: 10 hours  ✽  Makes 16 servings

Per serving: 243 calories, 8 g protein, 30 g carbohydrates, 12 g total fat, 5 g saturated fat, 2 g fiber, 397 mg sodium

Your guests will not believe that this creamy chocolate concoction is low in calories—so don't tell them!

# Italian Cheesecake with Toasted Pine Nuts

6 eggs, separated

¾ teaspoon cream of tartar

¾ cup sugar

2 teaspoons vanilla extract

1 container (32 ounces) part-skim ricotta cheese

2 tablespoons toasted pine nuts (see note page 98)

**PREHEAT** the oven to 325°F. Lightly coat a 9" round springform pan with cooking spray. Set on a baking sheet.

**IN** a large bowl, beat the egg whites with an electric mixer on high speed for about 1 minute, or until frothy. Add the cream of tartar and beat for 3 minutes, or until stiff peaks form.

**IN** a large bowl with an electric mixer and the unwashed beaters on medium speed, beat the egg yolks, sugar, and the vanilla for 1 minute. Add the ricotta and beat on high speed until smooth. Gently fold in one-third of the whites, then fold in the rest until combined. Spoon the batter into the springform pan.

**BAKE** for about 1 hour 10 minutes, or until the cake is golden and almost set in the middle.

**COOL** in the pan on a rack. Run a knife between the pan and the sides of the cake. Cover loosely and refrigerate for at least 4 hours.

**REMOVE** the sides of the pan. Sprinkle with the pine nuts before serving.

Total time: 5 hours 30 minutes ✽ Makes 12 servings

Per serving: 182 calories, 11 g protein, 17 g carbohydrates, 9 g total fat, 5 g saturated fat, 0 g fiber, 139 mg sodium

Eat cheesecake and lose weight? You bet. Savor this calcium-rich treat in moderation to stave off cravings.

# Chocolate-Nut Torte with Ganache

½ cup trans-free spread or butter

¼ cup sugar

4 eggs, separated

¾ cup ground almonds or walnuts

½ cup dry bread crumbs

6 ounces bittersweet chocolate, coarsely grated, divided

¼ cup prune juice

1½ teaspoons vanilla extract

¼ cup fat-free half-and-half

Sliced almonds or walnut pieces (optional)

**PREHEAT** the oven to 325°F. Line an 8" round cake pan with waxed paper.

**IN** a large bowl, stir together the spread or butter and sugar until light and fluffy. Stir in the egg yolks, nuts, bread crumbs, 4 ounces of the chocolate, the prune juice, and vanilla until smooth.

**IN** another large bowl, beat the egg whites with an electric mixer on high speed for about 3 minutes, or until stiff peaks form. Gently fold into the batter. Pour into the cake pan.

**BAKE** for about 40 minutes, or until a tester inserted in the center comes out clean. Cool in the pan on a rack for 5 minutes. Remove to the rack to cool for 30 minutes.

**MEANWHILE,** in a small saucepan over low heat, combine the half-and-half and the remaining 2 ounces chocolate. Cook and stir over low heat for about 2 minutes, or until the chocolate is melted. Remove from the heat and let stand for 2 minutes.

**SPREAD** the ganache over the top of the torte. Garnish with nut pieces (if using).

-------------------------------------------------------------------

Total time: 1 hour 45 minutes ✻ Makes 12 servings

Per serving: 225 calories, 5 g protein, 18 g carbohydrates, 17 g total fat, 5 g saturated fat, 2 g fiber, 123 mg sodium

The luxurious topping on this torte is sure to satisfy even the most hard-to-please chocoholic.

# Nectarine-Raspberry Dream

¾ cup toasted raw almonds, ground (see note page 98), divided

¾ cup sugar, divided

¼ cup trans-free spread or butter, softened

2 packages (8 ounces each) reduced-fat cream cheese

1 cup sugar-free fat-free raspberry yogurt

1 cup sugar-free fat-free peach or apricot yogurt

2 large nectarines, sliced

½ pint raspberries (optional)

PLACE ¼ cup of the nuts in a small bowl and set aside.

PLACE the remaining ½ cup nuts in another small bowl. Stir in ¼ cup of the sugar and the spread or butter. Press the mixture firmly into the bottom of an 8" round springform pan.

IN a large mixing bowl with an electric mixer on medium speed, beat the cream cheese and the remaining ½ cup of sugar until smooth. Remove half of the mixture to a medium bowl and whisk in the raspberry yogurt. Spread evenly over the nut crust. Place in the freezer for 1 hour, or until firm.

STIR the peach or apricot yogurt into the remaining cream cheese mixture. Spread over the frozen raspberry layer. Freeze for about 2 hours, or until firm.

REMOVE the tart to a large platter. Surround with the nectarines. Sprinkle with the remaining nuts and raspberries (if using).

--------------------------------------------------------------

Total time: 3 hours 40 minutes  ✱  Makes 10 servings

Per serving: 280 calories, 8 g protein, 28 g carbohydrates, 15 g total fat, 6 g saturated fat, 2 g fiber, 272 mg sodium

Incorporating fresh fruit—with its antioxidants and fiber—into desserts is always a smart approach.

# Black-Bottom Chocolate Brownie Torte

**Crust**

- ½ cup chocolate wafer cookie crumbs (10 cookies)
- 1 tablespoon granulated sugar
- 1 tablespoon canola oil

**Filling**

- ½ cup all-purpose flour
- 1 tablespoon unsweetened cocoa powder
- 1 teaspoon instant espresso coffee powder
- ½ teaspoon ground cinnamon
- 2 ounces bittersweet or semisweet chocolate
- ½ cup lite cream cheese
- ½ cup packed light brown sugar
- 1 tablespoon canola oil
- 1 teaspoon vanilla extract
- 2 eggs
  Confectioners' sugar (optional)

To make the crust:
PREHEAT the oven to 350°F. In a small bowl, stir together the cookie crumbs, sugar, and oil. Press into the bottom of an 8" round spring-form pan.

BAKE for 10 minutes. Cool in the pan on a rack.

To make the filling:
DECREASE the oven temperature to 325°F.

IN a small bowl, stir together the flour, cocoa, coffee powder, and cinnamon.

PLACE the chocolate in a microwaveable bowl. Microwave on high power for about 1 minute, or until just melted.

IN a medium bowl, beat together the cream cheese, brown sugar, oil, and vanilla. A little bit at a time, beat in the eggs and chocolate until smooth. Stir in the flour mixture just until blended. Spread the batter evenly into the pan.

BAKE for 30 to 35 minutes, or until a wooden pick inserted in the center comes out almost clean. Cool in the pan on a rack for 10 minutes. Run a knife between the cake and the sides of the pan. Remove the sides of the pan. Cool for 10 minutes.

DUST with the confectioners' sugar (if using).

-------------------------------------------------------------

Total time: 1 hour 10 minutes  ✱  Makes 8 servings

Per serving: 234 calories, 5 g protein, 32 g carbohydrates, 11 g total fat, 4 g saturated fat, 1 g fiber, 129 mg sodium

For special times, this dessert is sure to be a big hit with kids and grown-ups alike.

# Apple Crumb Pie

¾ cup all-purpose flour

2 tablespoons cold trans-free spread or butter

¼ cup packed light brown sugar

1 teaspoon pumpkin pie spice, divided

½ cup granulated sugar

2½ tablespoons quick-cooking tapioca

6 Granny Smith apples, peeled and sliced

1 prepared pie crust (9" diameter)

PREHEAT the oven to 425°F.

IN a medium bowl, combine the flour and spread or butter. With a pastry blender or fork, blend until coarse crumbs form. Stir in the brown sugar and ¼ teaspoon of the spice.

IN a large bowl, stir together the granulated sugar, tapioca, and the remaining ¾ teaspoon spice. Toss in the apples to coat with the dry ingredients. Spoon into the crust. Sprinkle with the crumb topping.

BAKE for 10 minutes. Reduce the oven temperature to 350°F and bake for 30 minutes, or until golden brown and bubbling. Cool in the pan on a rack.

- - - - - - - - - - - - - - - - - - - - - - - - - - - - - - - - - - - - - - - - - - - - - - - -

Total time: 50 minutes ✱ Makes 8 servings

Per serving: 296 calories, 3 g protein, 55 g carbohydrates, 8 g total fat, 2 g saturated fat, 3 g fiber, 113 mg sodium

No pastry-making trauma with this all-American beauty. Start with a prepared crust and blanket the fruit with an easy crumb topping.

⎡ **SUPERFOOD SPOTLIGHT: APPLES** ⎤

**Taste them:** Though available from cold storage all year, apples are at their flavor- and nutrition-packed peak from September through November.

**Love them:** A single apple packs a wallop of vitamin C and cancer-fighting antioxidants, as well as more fiber than a bowl of bran cereal—for fewer than 100 calories each.

**Store them:** Apples need to be refrigerated. Although lovely arranged in a bowl on the table, they'll become soft if left out at room temperature.

# Lemon Meringue Pie

6 tablespoons cornstarch

¾ cup sugar, divided

1½ cups water

½ cup lemon juice

4 eggs

2 teaspoons grated lemon peel

6 egg whites, at room temperature

⅛ teaspoon cream of tartar

½ teaspoon vanilla extract

1 prebaked pie crust (9" diameter)

**PREHEAT** the oven to 350°F.

**IN** a medium saucepan, whisk the cornstarch with ½ cup of the sugar. Whisk in the water and lemon juice until the sugar is dissolved. Cook and whisk over medium heat for about 3 minutes, or until the mixture comes to a boil and thickens slightly. Remove from the heat.

**IN** a mixing bowl, whisk the eggs and lemon peel. Whisking constantly, gradually add the hot lemon mixture. Pour into the pan and cook on medium heat, whisking constantly, for about 2 minutes, or until thickened. Let stand, whisking occasionally, for about 10 minutes, or until cooled to room temperature.

**IN** a mixing bowl, beat the egg whites with an electric mixer on high speed for 1 minute, or until foamy. Add the cream of tartar and beat for 2 minutes, or until soft peaks form. Beat, adding the remaining ¼ cup sugar, 1 tablespoon at a time, and the vanilla for about 1 minute, or until stiff peaks form.

**SPOON** the lemon filling into the crust. Smooth the top. Spread the whites over the filling, touching the crust around the edge. With the back of a spoon, make peaks in the whites.

**BAKE** for about 8 minutes, or until golden. Cool in the pan on a rack.

Total time: 25 minutes   *   Makes 8 servings

Per serving: 300 calories, 8 g protein, 45 g carbohydrates, 10 g total fat, 3 g saturated fat, 1 g fiber, 190 mg sodium

Scrub lemons well under very warm water to remove any wax adhering to the peel. Potent with lemon oil, the peel is a great flavor booster.

**QUICK TIP: PEER PRESSURE**

104% How much harder you're likely to work out when you exercise with a pal

# Chocolate Cream Banana Pie

½ cup all-fiber cereal crumbs

⅛ teaspoon ground cinnamon

1½ tablespoons cold trans-free spread or butter

¼ cup packed light brown sugar

2½ tablespoons cornstarch

2 cups fat free milk

1 egg

2 ounces bittersweet chocolate, chopped

1 teaspoon vanilla extract

1 banana

Fat-free whipped cream (optional)

COAT a pie pan with cooking spray.

IN a small bowl, combine the crumbs and cinnamon with a fork. Cut in the spread or butter until well blended. Transfer to the pan. Tilt the pan to coat the sides with crumbs. Press the remaining crumbs with your knuckles to flatten evenly. Set in the freezer for 30 minutes.

MEANWHILE, in a saucepan, whisk together the sugar and cornstarch. In a bowl, whisk the milk and egg. Add to the pan, whisking constantly, until blended. Cook and whisk over medium heat for about 5 minutes, or until thickened. Remove from the heat. Whisk in the chocolate and vanilla until the chocolate melts. Let stand, stirring occasionally, to cool completely.

CUT the banana into thin slices. Arrange on the bottom and sides of the crust. Dollop the pudding into the pan. Refrigerate for at least 5 hours, or until set.

SERVE each slice garnished with 1 tablespoon whipped cream (if using).

Total time: 6 hours ✳ Makes 8 servings

Per serving: 144 calories, 4 g protein, 20 g carbohydrates, 7 g total fat, 3 g saturated fat, 3 g fiber, 69 mg sodium

You can make this pie in stages to fit into your busy schedule. Although you need to allow time for cooling and chilling the pudding, the actual preparation is a snap.

# Perfect Pumpkin Pie

8 sheets frozen whole wheat phyllo dough (14" × 9"), thawed

⅓ cup sugar

1 teaspoon ground cinnamon

¾ teaspoon ground ginger

Pinch of salt

½ teaspoon ground allspice

1 can (15 ounces) pumpkin puree

3 egg whites

1 egg

1 can (12 ounces) fat-free evaporated milk

2 tablespoons maple syrup

2 teaspoons vanilla extract

Fat-free whipped topping (optional)

Bittersweet chocolate for shavings (optional)

**PREHEAT** the oven to 350°F. Lightly coat a 9" pie pan with cooking spray.

**STACK** the phyllo on plastic wrap or waxed paper and cover with a lightly dampened towel.

**LAY** 1 sheet of phyllo in the pie pan. Coat the sheet with cooking spray, making sure to spray the edges. Repeat with the remaining sheets, rotating each slightly in the pan to form a circle. Fold and crimp the edges. Place a piece of parchment or waxed paper on top of the crust. Fill the pan with pie weights or dried beans.

**BAKE** for about 10 minutes, or until the edges are lightly golden. Remove to a rack.

**MEANWHILE,** in a medium bowl, stir together the sugar, cinnamon, ginger, salt, and allspice. Set aside.

**IN** a large bowl, whisk together the pumpkin, egg whites, and egg. Whisk while slowly adding the milk, syrup, and vanilla until blended. Whisk in the reserved dry mixture.

**REMOVE** the pie weights from the crust. Pour in the filling.

**BAKE** for 50 minutes to 1 hour, or until a tester inserted in the center comes out clean. Cool in the pan on a rack.

**SERVE** with whipped topping (if using) and chocolate shavings (if using).

Total time: 1 hour 20 minutes ✳ Makes 8 servings

Per serving: 152 calories, 6 g protein, 31 g carbohydrates, 1 g total fat, 0 g saturated fat, 2 g fiber, 162 mg sodium

Who needs regular pie crust when the real attraction of traditional pumpkin pie is the spicy, creamy filling? We swap phyllo for fat-laden pastry in this version.

# Frozen Strawberry Pie

6½ ounces vanilla wafers

2 tablespoons trans-free spread or butter, melted

2 tablespoons canola oil

1 package (8 ounces) reduced-fat cream cheese, at room temperature

½ cup confectioners' sugar

1 pint strawberries

1 tablespoon granulated sugar

**IN** a food processor, process the wafers for about 2 minutes, or until fine crumbs form. Add the spread or butter and oil. Pulse for 30 seconds, or until blended. Press the mixture firmly into the bottom and sides of a 9" pie pan. Refrigerate for 20 minutes.

**PREHEAT** the oven to 325°F. Bake the crust for about 16 minutes, or until golden. Cool in the pan on a rack.

**IN** a mixing bowl with an electric mixer on medium speed, beat the cream cheese until smooth. On low speed, beat in the confectioners' sugar. Increase the speed to medium for about 30 seconds, or until smooth.

**PROCESS** one-quarter of the strawberries in a food processor for about 2 minutes, or until pureed. Fold into the cream cheese mixture. Pour into the crust. Freeze for about 1½ hours, or until just firm.

**HALVE** or quarter the remaining berries and place in a medium bowl. Add the granulated sugar and toss to combine. Let stand at least 5 minutes. Slice the pie and top with the berries.

Total time: 2 hours 15 minutes  ✱  Makes 8 servings

Per serving: 293 calories, 4 g protein, 31 g carbohydrates, 18 g total fat, 7 g saturated fat, 2 g fiber, 205 mg sodium

## GOTTA TRY IT! THE POWER OF FRIENDS

Rather than gabbing with friends over coffee or wine, pair conversation with calorie burning instead. Seattleite Bonny Becker and five of her BFFs gather for personal training sessions, hikes, or bike rides every week. "We've walked the Portland Marathon and tried rock climbing together," she says. By forming a fitness club or adding exercise to your get-togethers—like launching each book club meeting with a walk—you'll motivate the gang to work out more often and grow closer, too.

# Blueberries and Lime Cream Tart

2 tablespoons honey

2 teaspoons cornstarch

1½ cups fresh or frozen and thawed blueberries

¼ cup all-fiber cereal crumbs

⅛ teaspoon ground cinnamon

1 tablespoon cold trans-free spread or butter

1 package (8 ounces) reduced-fat cream cheese, at room temperature

2 tablespoons confectioners' sugar

2 tablespoons lime juice

1 teaspoon grated lime peel

COAT an 8" springform pan with cooking spray. Set aside.

IN a saucepan, stir together the honey and cornstarch. Add the blueberries. Cook over medium heat, stirring gently, for about 4 minutes, or until the mixture bubbles. Remove and let stand to cool to room temperature.

MEANWHILE, in a small bowl, combine the crumbs and cinnamon with a fork. Cut in the spread or butter until well blended. Press the mixture firmly into the bottom of the springform pan. Set in the freezer for 30 minutes.

MEANWHILE, in a mixing bowl, stir together the cream cheese, sugar, lime juice, and lime peel. Slowly mix by hand to soften, then beat until very smooth. Spread evenly in the pan. Spread evenly with the blueberry mixture.

COVER and refrigerate for 3 hours, or until set.

Total time: 4 hours 10 minutes ✱ Makes 8 servings

Per serving: 114 calories, 3 g protein, 16 g carbohydrates, 0 g total fat, 3 g saturated fat, 3 g fiber, 130 mg sodium

⌐ **QUICK TIP: THE RIGHT MATCH** ⌐

Head off cravings and binges by pairing protein with good carbs at every meal, says Sari Greaves, RD, a spokesperson for the American Dietetic Association. For snacks, try 0% Greek yogurt sprinkled with berries or pretzels with hummus. Both are healthy combos of protein and carbs, which will reduce levels of hunger hormones so you don't have cravings.

# Peach and Raspberry Crostata

**Crust**

1½ cups whole grain pastry flour

¼ teaspoon salt

¼ cup cold trans-free spread or butter, cut into small pieces

2 ounces reduced-fat cream cheese

5 tablespoons ice water, divided

2 teaspoons lemon juice

**Filling**

3 tablespoons shredded bran cereal

1 tablespoon whole grain pastry flour

¼ teaspoon ground cinnamon

6 tablespoons sugar, divided

1¾ pounds peaches, sliced

1 cup raspberries

To make the crust:

**IN** a large bowl, stir together the flour and salt. Cut in the spread or butter and cream cheese until the mixture resembles coarse crumbs. In a cup, stir together 2 tablespoons of the water and the lemon juice. Drizzle over the crumb mixture and mix until moistened. Mix in the remaining 3 tablespoons water, 1 tablespoon at a time, until the dough can be pressed into a firm ball. Press into a disk. Cover with plastic wrap and refrigerate for 30 minutes.

**PLACE** a wide sheet of foil on a large baking sheet and coat with cooking spray. Fold the edges of the foil up ½" to form a rim. Roll the dough out between sheets of lightly floured waxed paper to a 13" circle. Place on the foil.

To make the filling:

**PREHEAT** the oven to 400°F.

**IN** a food processor or blender, combine the cereal, flour, cinnamon, and 4 tablespoons of the sugar. Process or blend for about 90 seconds, or until finely ground. Sprinkle over the pastry, leaving a 2" border. Arrange the peaches on top. Fold the pastry border over the fruit. Sprinkle with the remaining 2 tablespoons sugar.

**BAKE** for about 45 minutes, or until the crust is golden brown and the juices are bubbling. Cool in the pan on a rack. Sprinkle with the raspberries.

---

Total time: 1 hour 55 minutes ✽ Makes 10 servings

Per serving: 179 calories, 4 g protein, 29 g carbohydrates, 6 g total fat, 3 g saturated fat, 4 g fiber, 75 mg sodium

This pie is inspired by European country-style free-form fruit tarts, so there's no pressure to create a picture-perfect crust. The more rustic it looks, the better.

# Plum Strudel

¾ cup sugar, divided

¼ cup chopped walnuts, toasted (see note page 98)

1 teaspoon ground cinnamon

1⅓ pounds Italian purple plums or red-skinned plums, sliced

⅓ cup plum preserves

¼ cup all-purpose flour

2 teaspoons grated orange peel

8 sheets phyllo dough, thawed if frozen

**PREHEAT** the oven to 400°F. Line a baking sheet with foil and coat with cooking spray.

**IN** a food processor or blender, combine ¼ cup of the sugar, the walnuts, and cinnamon. Process or blend for 1 to 2 minutes, or until the walnuts are finely ground.

**IN** a large bowl, stir together the plums, preserves, flour, orange peel, and the remaining ½ cup sugar until the sugar is dissolved.

**PLACE** a double layer of phyllo on a work surface with one of the long edges facing you. (Cover the remaining sheets with a lightly dampened dish towel to keep them from drying out.) Coat with cooking spray. Sprinkle with 2 tablespoons of the walnut mixture. Repeat 3 times with the remaining phyllo and walnut mixture.

**SPOON** the plum mixture lengthwise down the center third of the phyllo, leaving a 2" border at the top and bottom (along the long sides). Pick up one of the short sides and fold the phyllo over the plum mixture. Fold the other short side over the phyllo. Starting from the end closest to you, tightly roll the phyllo away from you into a cylinder. Place the strudel, seam side down, on the baking pan. Coat with cooking spray.

**BAKE** for about 45 minutes, or until golden brown and crispy. Cool in the pan on a rack for 10 minutes.

Total time: 1 hour 15 minutes  ✱  Makes 8 servings

Per serving: 237 calories, 3 g protein, 50 g carbohydrates, 4 g total fat, 0 g saturated fat, 2 g fiber, 92 mg sodium

## QUICK TIP: EASY AS 1, 2, 3

3 The number of whole walnuts that supplies your daily goal for omega-3 fats

# Nectarine-Raspberry Crisp

3 pounds nectarines, sliced

½ pint fresh or frozen and thawed raspberries

¾ cup sugar, divided

1 tablespoon cornstarch

½ teaspoon almond extract

½ teaspoon ground ginger

½ cup quick-cooking oats

½ cup whole grain pastry flour

3 tablespoons sliced almonds

¼ teaspoon salt

3 tablespoons cold trans-free spread or butter, cut into small pieces

2 teaspoons water

PREHEAT the oven to 375°F. Coat an 11" × 7" baking dish with cooking spray.

IN a large bowl, stir together the nectarines, raspberries, ½ cup of the sugar, the cornstarch, almond extract, and ginger. Pour into the baking dish.

IN a separate bowl, stir together the oats, flour, almonds, salt, and the remaining ¼ cup sugar. Rub in the spread or butter with your fingertips until the mixture resembles coarse crumbs. Rub in the water and firmly press the mixture into clumps. Break the clumps into smaller pieces and scatter them evenly over the nectarine mixture.

BAKE for about 40 minutes, or until golden and the filling is bubbling. Serve warm or at room temperature.

----

Total time: 1 hour  ✱  Makes 12 servings

Per serving: 155 calories, 3 g protein, 30 g carbohydrates, 5 g total fat, 2 g saturated fat, 4 g fiber, 50 mg sodium

## QUICK TIP: BETTER CRAVING CONTROL
According to new research, the brain chemicals that signal the body to stop eating rise after exercise, so you eat less.

# Summer Fruit Turnovers

1 pint strawberries, sliced

½ pint raspberries

⅔ cup sugar

3 tablespoons all-purpose flour

1½ tablespoons lemon juice

8 sheets phyllo dough, thawed if frozen

PREHEAT the oven to 400°F. Line a baking sheet with foil and coat with cooking spray.

IN a medium bowl, stir together the strawberries, raspberries, sugar, flour, and lemon juice until the sugar is dissolved.

PLACE a double layer of phyllo on a work surface with one of the long edges facing you. (Cover the remaining sheets with a lightly dampened dish towel to keep them from drying out.) Coat with cooking spray. Top with 2 more sheets and coat with cooking spray.

CUT the prepared sheets from top to bottom (not from left to right) into 3 equal strips. Place ½ cup of the fruit mixture at the bottom of each strip. Fold the lower right corner to the opposite edge to form a triangle. Continue to fold the triangle up the length of the strip until you reach the end. Coat with cooking spray and transfer to the prepared pan. Repeat with the remaining phyllo and filling to make a total of 6 turnovers.

BAKE for about 20 minutes, or until golden brown and crispy. Cool on the pan on a rack for 10 minutes.

Total time: 1 hour 5 minutes ✱ Makes 6 servings

Per serving: 205 calories, 3 g protein, 46 g carbohydrates, 2 g total fat, 0 g saturated fat, 3 g fiber, 123 mg sodium

The contrast of crackling crisp pastry and soft sweet berries is delightful.

# Apple-Cranberry Crisp

½ cup water

⅓ cup dried cranberries

½ cup old-fashioned rolled oats

½ cup trans-free spread or butter

½ cup whole grain pastry flour, divided

¼ cup + 2 tablespoons sugar

2 teaspoons ground cinnamon, divided

8 Golden Delicious apples, sliced

1½ teaspoons vanilla extract

½ teaspoon ground nutmeg

Fat-free whipped topping (optional)

**PREHEAT** the oven to 350°F. Lightly coat a 13" × 9" baking dish with cooking spray.

**IN** a small bowl, combine the water and cranberries. Set aside.

**MEANWHILE,** in a medium bowl, combine the oats, spread or butter, ¼ cup of the flour, ¼ cup of the sugar, and 1 teaspoon of the cinnamon. With a fork or pastry blender, stir until the mixture is crumbly.

**IN** a large bowl, stir together the apples, vanilla, nutmeg, and the remaining ¼ cup flour, 2 tablespoons sugar, and 1 teaspoon cinnamon. Toss to coat the apples evenly with the dry ingredients.

**PLACE** the mixture in the baking dish. Pour the reserved water and cranberries evenly into the pan. Sprinkle evenly with the oat topping.

**BAKE** for about 40 minutes, or until the topping is golden and the juices are bubbling. Remove to a rack to cool in the pan for 15 minutes. Serve warm with whipped topping (if using).

------

Total time: 1 hour 5 minutes  ✱  Makes 12 servings

Per serving: 170 calories, 2 g protein, 27 g carbohydrates, 7 g total fat, 2 g saturated fat, 3 g fiber, 65 mg sodium

Any leftover crisp makes a terrific snack when topped with a dollop of thick 0% plain Greek yogurt.

# Sumptuous Strawberry Crepes

8 packaged crepes

4 ounces fat-free cream cheese

1 cup fat-free sour cream

¼ cup packed light brown sugar

½ teaspoon vanilla extract

1 teaspoon grated orange peel

1½ pints strawberries, sliced

1 tablespoon honey

**PLACE** the crepes on a microwaveable plate. Cover with waxed paper. Microwave on high power for 1 minute, or until heated.

**IN** a food processor or blender, combine the cream cheese, sour cream, sugar, vanilla, and orange peel. Process or blend for about 1 minute, scraping the sides of the bowl as needed, or until smooth. Spread a small amount of the mixture inside each crepe. Divide 2 cups of the strawberries among the crepes. Roll up and place seam side down in a serving dish.

**IN** a blender or food processor, combine the remaining strawberries and honey. Process or blend for about 1 minute, or until a chunky sauce forms. Drizzle over the crepes.

Total time: 10 minutes ✳ Makes 4 servings

Per serving: 242 calories, 9 g protein, 49 g carbohydrates, 2 g total fat, 0 g saturated fat, 3 g fiber, 347 mg sodium

Start with prepared crepes and you have a company-worthy dessert ready in 10 minutes.

# Chocolate Bread Pudding

4 slices day-old oatmeal bread, cubed

2 cups fat-free milk

¾ cup packed dark brown sugar

¼ cup unsweetened cocoa powder

3 eggs

1½ teaspoons vanilla extract

Confectioners' sugar (optional)

PREHEAT the oven to 350°F. Coat an 8" × 8" nonstick baking pan with cooking spray.

SCATTER the bread into the baking pan.

HEAT the milk in a small saucepan until almost boiling.

IN a medium bowl, stir together the brown sugar and cocoa. Gradually add the milk, whisking constantly, until the sugar is dissolved. Whisk in the eggs and vanilla. Pour over the bread. Press the bread down gently to soak evenly.

BAKE for about 35 minutes, or until set. Cool in the pan on a rack for 10 minutes. Lightly dust the top with confectioners' sugar (if using). Serve warm.

Total time: 1 hour 20 minutes  ✴  Makes 8 servings

Per serving: 190 calories, 6 g protein, 35 g carbohydrates, 3 g total fat, 1 g saturated fat, 1 g fiber, 180 mg sodium

Two childhood comfort dishes—chocolate pudding and bread pudding—come together in this totally grown-up dessert.

# Coconut Rice Pudding with Dates

2 cans (12 ounces each) evaporated fat-free milk

1 egg

¼ cup packed light brown sugar

2 teaspoons coconut extract

½ cup brown rice

⅓ cup chopped dates

Fat-free whipped cream (optional)

8 teaspoons flaked coconut (optional)

**PREHEAT** the oven to 325°F. Lightly coat an 8" × 8" baking dish with cooking spray. Heat the milk in a small saucepan until almost boiling.

**IN** a large bowl, whisk the egg. Add about ½ cup of the milk, whisking constantly, to warm the egg. Whisk in the sugar, coconut extract, and the remaining milk until smooth. Pour into the baking dish. Add the rice and dates. Stir with a fork. Cover with foil.

**BAKE** for 1 hour 15 minutes. Turn off the heat. Let stand in the oven for 30 minutes.

**GARNISH** with whipped cream (if using) and coconut (if using).

------------------------------------

Total time: 1 hour 55 minutes ✱ Makes 8 servings

Per serving: 161 calories, 7 g protein, 31 g carbohydrates, 1 g total fat, 0 g saturated fat, 1 g fiber, 116 mg sodium

This sweet tropical pudding is appealing when it's warm and creamy from the oven. But chilled leftovers are also fabulous garnished with a few slices of ripe mango or peach.

# Hot Chocolate Soufflé

⅓ cup granulated sugar

3 tablespoons unsweetened cocoa powder

1 tablespoon cornstarch

¾ cup fat-free milk

2 egg yolks

2 tablespoons water

2 teaspoons rum extract

5 egg whites

½ teaspoon cream of tartar

1 tablespoon confectioners' sugar

**PREHEAT** the oven to 375°F.

**IN** a large saucepan, stir together the sugar, cocoa, and cornstarch. Gradually add the milk, whisking constantly, until the dry ingredients are dissolved. Cook and whisk over medium heat for about 4 minutes, or until the mixture comes to a boil and thickens.

**IN** a small bowl, whisk together the egg yolks, water, and rum extract. Whisk in about one-quarter of the chocolate mixture. Pour into the saucepan. Cook and whisk for 1 minute to heat the yolks. Remove from the heat.

**IN** a mixing bowl with an electric mixer on high speed, beat the egg whites for about 1 minute, or until foamy. Add the cream of tartar and beat for about 2 minutes more, or until stiff peaks form. Fold one-quarter of the mixture into the chocolate mixture. Gently fold in the remaining egg white mixture. Spoon into a 1-quart soufflé dish.

**BAKE** for about 30 minutes, or until puffed and lightly browned. Dust with the confectioners' sugar.

-------------------------------------

Total time: 1 hour ✱ Makes 4 servings

Per serving: 170 calories, 8 g protein, 26 g carbohydrates, 3 g total fat, 1 g saturated fat, 1 g fiber, 99 mg sodium

If you own an electric mixer, you can make a soufflé. For especially fluffy beaten egg whites, let the eggs stand at room temperature for 30 minutes before whipping.

# Rum Tiramisu

6 egg whites

½ teaspoon cream of tartar

⅛ teaspoon salt

⅓ cup + 2 teaspoons sugar, divided

1½ teaspoons rum extract, divided

6 tablespoons whole grain pastry flour

½ cup part-skim ricotta cheese

¾ cup fat-free whipped topping

¼ cup brewed decaffeinated espresso, cooled

2 ounces bittersweet chocolate, finely grated

Mint sprigs for garnish (optional)

**PREHEAT** the oven to 350°F. Lightly coat an 8" × 8" baking pan with cooking spray.

**IN** a large bowl with an electric mixer at high speed, beat the egg whites, cream of tartar, and salt for about 3 minutes, or until soft peaks form. Add ⅓ cup sugar and ½ teaspoon of the rum extract. Beat for about 2 minutes, or until stiff peaks form. Sift 2 tablespoons of the flour over the egg whites and gently fold to incorporate. Repeat twice with the remaining flour until all of the flour is incorporated.

**POUR** the batter into the baking pan and smooth the top. Bake for about 20 minutes, or until the cake is golden and a tester inserted in the center comes out clean. Cool in the pan on a rack.

**IN** a small bowl, stir together the ricotta, whipped topping, the remaining 2 teaspoons sugar, and 1 teaspoon rum extract. Cut the cake in half down the middle to make two 8" × 4" pieces. Place the cake pieces on a work surface. Drizzle with the espresso. Spread half of the ricotta mixture over 1 piece, sprinkle with half of the chocolate, and top with the remaining cake. Spread on the remaining ricotta mixture and sprinkle with the remaining chocolate. Garnish with mint leaves (if using).

--------------------------------------

Total time: 1 hour 10 minutes ✱ Makes 4 servings

Per serving: 273 calories, 12 g protein, 39 g carbohydrates, 9 g total fat, 5 g saturated fat, 2 g fiber, 197 mg sodium

Usually this Italian extravagance is made with mascarpone, a fresh cheese that contains almost as much fat as butter! We think part-skim ricotta cheese is a better idea.

# Lemon Gelatin Whip

2 boxes (0.3 ounces each) sugar-free lemon gelatin

2 cups boiling water

1 cup cold water

⅓ cup reduced-fat sour cream

⅓ cup part-skim ricotta cheese

⅓ cup reduced-fat cream cheese

½ teaspoon lemon extract

IN a mixing bowl, whisk together the gelatin and boiling water until dissolved. Whisk in the cold water. Pour into an 8" × 8" ceramic or glass dish. Cover and refrigerate for several hours, or until firm.

IN a blender or food processor, combine the sour cream, ricotta, cream cheese, and lemon extract. Blend or process, scraping the sides of the bowl as needed, until light and fluffy. Cut the gelatin into sections and add to the blender or food processor. Blend or process on high speed for about 4 minutes, or until smooth and frothy. Divide among 6 serving bowls. Cover and refrigerate for at least 1 hour.

Total time: 3 hours 10 minutes  ✱  Makes 6 servings

Per serving: 82 calories, 5 g protein, 2 g carbohydrates, 5 g total fat, 3 g saturated fat, 0 g fiber, 139 mg sodium

This frothy delight keeps well in the refrigerator for up to 3 days, so you can have it on hand for an easy end-of-the-day treat that weighs in at fewer than 100 calories.

# Strawberry Cream Clouds

3 egg whites

¼ teaspoon salt

½ cup + 1 tablespoon granulated sugar, divided

1 pint strawberries, sliced

¾ cup whipping cream

¼ cup confectioners' sugar

¼ teaspoon almond extract

2 tablespoons sliced almonds, toasted (see note page 98)

**PREHEAT** the oven to 200°F. Line 2 large baking sheets with parchment paper.

**IN** a mixing bowl, combine the egg whites and salt. Beat on high speed with an electric mixer for 2 minutes, or until soft peaks form. Gradually add ½ cup of the granulated sugar, beating for about 2 minutes, or until stiff peaks form. Spoon onto the baking sheets in 8 mounds (4" diameter). With the back of a spoon, make small hollows in the mounds.

**BAKE** for 1½ hours, or until set. Turn off the oven and let cool in the oven for 1 hour.

**MEANWHILE,** in a medium bowl, stir together the strawberries and the remaining 1 tablespoon granulated sugar. Cover and refrigerate.

**IN** a mixing bowl, combine the cream, confectioners' sugar, and almond extract. Beat with an electric mixer on high speed for about 2 minutes, or until stiff peaks form.

**REMOVE** the meringues from the oven and divide among 8 dessert plates. Divide the strawberries and whipped cream on top. Sprinkle with the almonds.

----

Total time: 3 hours 15 minutes ✳ Makes 8 servings

Per serving: 175 calories, 2 g protein, 22 g carbohydrates, 9 g total fat, 5 g saturated fat, 1 g fiber, 102 mg sodium

These meringue desserts are a generous 4" in diameter, so they seem really decadent. And they certainly don't taste like diet food—not with that luscious mound of whipped cream.

# Mango-Banana Mousse

2 **very ripe mangoes, coarsely chopped**

½ **cup fat-free vanilla yogurt**

1 **small very ripe banana**

2 **teaspoons honey**

⅛ **teaspoon vanilla extract**

3 **ice cubes**

4 **sprigs mint**

½ **cup raspberries (optional)**

**IN** a food processor or blender, combine the mangoes, yogurt, banana, honey, vanilla, and ice cubes. Pulse for about 45 seconds, or until the ice is broken up. Process or blend for about 1 minute, or until smooth. Remove and discard any pieces of ice.

**DIVIDE** the mixture among 4 dessert dishes. Garnish with the mint and raspberries (if using).

----

Total time: 15 minutes ✸ Makes 4 servings

Per serving: 128 calories, 2 g protein, 32 g carbohydrates, 0 g total fat, 0 g saturated fat, 3 g fiber, 24 mg sodium

If mangoes aren't ripe, store them at room temperature in a fruit bowl or brown paper bag with some bananas until the mangoes are soft when gently pressed.

# Peanut Butter Cup Mousse

1½ cups 1% milk, divided

½ cup packed light brown sugar, divided

3 tablespoons cornstarch

1 egg

2 tablespoons creamy peanut butter

⅛ teaspoon salt

2 teaspoons vanilla extract

1 cup fat-free refrigerated whipped topping

2 tablespoons chocolate chips, melted

1 tablespoon finely chopped roasted unsalted peanuts

IN a small bowl, whisk together ½ cup of the milk, ¼ cup of the sugar, the cornstarch, and egg.

IN a medium saucepan over medium heat, stir together the peanut butter, salt, and the remaining 1 cup milk and ¼ cup sugar. Cook and whisk for about 3 minutes, or until the mixture boils. Gradually pour in the cornstarch mixture and cook, whisking constantly, for about 5 minutes, or until thickened. Remove from the heat and stir in the vanilla. Let cool to room temperature.

FOLD the whipped topping into the peanut butter mixture. Divide among 4 serving bowls. Cover and refrigerate for about 1 hour, or until set.

DRIZZLE with the melted chocolate and sprinkle with the peanuts.

---

Total time: 1 hour 40 minutes ✳ Makes 4 servings

Per serving: 291 calories, 7 g protein, 46 g carbohydrates, 9 g total fat, 3 g saturated fat, 1 g fiber, 178 mg sodium

Who needs candy bars when you can have the same yummy taste and texture in this calorie-trimmed dessert?

# Coconut Custard Brûlée

⅓ cup confectioners' sugar

¼ cup cornstarch

2½ cups canned light coconut milk

3 eggs

Dash of salt

1½ teaspoons coconut extract

2 tablespoons packed light brown sugar

**COAT** six ½-cup heatproof custard cups or ramekins with cooking spray. Place them on a rimmed baking pan.

**IN** a saucepan, combine the confectioners' sugar and cornstarch. Whisking constantly, gradually add the coconut milk until the mixture is smooth. Pass through a fine sieve set over a bowl or large measuring cup. With a spatula, press any lumps of cornstarch or sugar through the sieve. Return to the pan.

**WHISK** in the eggs and salt. Cook and stir over medium heat for about 5 minutes, or until the mixture bubbles and thickens.

**REMOVE** from the heat, whisking to cool down the mixture. Stir in the coconut extract. Divide among the custard cups. With the back of a small spoon, smooth the tops to flatten. Cover with plastic wrap and refrigerate for at least 4 hours, or until cold.

**PREHEAT** the broiler. Sprinkle the brown sugar evenly over the tops of the custards. Broil for about 1 minute, or until the sugar is caramelized. Watch carefully so the sugar doesn't burn.

---

Total time: 4 hours 15 minutes  ✻  Makes 6 servings

Per serving: 156 calories, 4 g protein, 20 g carbohydrates, 8 g total fat, 5 g saturated fat, 0 g fiber, 112 mg sodium

# Fruit Compote
# with Sugared Wonton Cookies

1 pint blackberries

1 pint blueberries

1 banana, sliced

1 peach, sliced

2 tablespoons maple syrup

1 tablespoon chopped fresh mint

1 teaspoon lime juice or lemon juice

4 wonton wrappers

2 tablespoons sugar

**PREHEAT** the oven to 425°F.

**IN** a large bowl, stir together the blackberries, blueberries, banana, peach, syrup, mint, and lime juice or lemon juice. Let stand at room temperature, stirring occasionally, for 20 minutes.

**PLACE** the wonton wrappers on a baking sheet. Coat both sides with cooking spray. Sprinkle with the sugar. Bake for 5 minutes, or until the edges start to turn color. Turn and bake for 2 minutes, or until golden brown and crisp.

**DIVIDE** the wontons and fruit among 4 dessert plates.

-------------------------------------------

Total time: 35 minutes ✱ Makes 4 servings

Per serving: 195 calories, 3 g protein, 47 g carbohydrates, 1 g total fat, 0 g saturated fat, 8 g fiber, 49 mg sodium

In the wintertime, loose-pack frozen berries and peaches can take the place of the fresh fruit.

# Baked Apples with Raisins

4 large Granny Smith apples,
  unpeeled and halved

¼ cup dark raisins

3 tablespoons sugar

2 tablespoons trans-free spread
  or butter, cut into small pieces

½ teaspoon ground cinnamon

**PREHEAT** the oven to 350°F. Coat a 13" × 9" baking dish with cooking spray. Place the apples, skin side down, in the dish.

**IN** a small bowl, mix together the raisins, sugar, spread or butter, and cinnamon until crumbly. Divide among the apple cavities. Pour 1 cup water into the baking dish.

**BAKE** for about 45 minutes, or until the apples are tender when pierced with a small sharp knife. Cool in the baking dish on a rack for 30 minutes.

-------------------------------------------------------------------

Total time: 1 hour 30 minutes  ✳  Makes 4 servings

Per serving: 231 calories, 1 g protein, 48 g carbohydrates, 6 g total fat,
4 g saturated fat, 6 g fiber, 4 mg sodium

You can refrigerate the baked fruit for several days. To reheat, place a cooked apple on a work surface and cut into slices or wedges. Place in a microwaveable bowl and drizzle with some of the cooking liquid. Microwave on medium power for 2 to 3 minutes, or until warmed through.

# Grilled Peaches with Macaroons and Caramel Sauce

4 peaches, halved

4 coconut macaroons

¼ cup jarred caramel topping

**COAT** a grill rack with cooking spray. Preheat the grill to medium.

**PLACE** the peaches, cut side down, on the grill rack. Grill for about 10 minutes, turning once, or until lightly browned.

**DIVIDE** the peaches among 4 dessert plates and crumble the macaroons on top. Drizzle with the caramel topping.

---

Total time: 15 minutes ✱ Makes 4 servings

Per serving: 209 calories, 2 g protein, 46 g carbohydrates, 4 g total fat, 3 g saturated fat, 3 g fiber, 131 mg sodium

Cooking familiar foods in new and different ways helps to maintain our enthusiasm for healthier eating. Try peaches on the grill at your next cookout.

# Berry and Peach Sundaes

¼ pint raspberries (½ cup)

¼ pint blueberries (½ cup)

1 peach, sliced

1 tablespoon sugar

2 cups low-fat vanilla ice cream

4 tablespoons seedless strawberry jam, warmed

2 tablespoons walnuts, coarsely chopped

IN a medium bowl, stir together the raspberries, blueberries, peach, and sugar. Cover and refrigerate, stirring occasionally, for 1 hour, or until the berry juices are syrupy.

DIVIDE the ice cream among 4 dessert bowls. Top with the fruit mixture, jam, and walnuts.

------

Total time: 1 hour 10 minutes  ✳  Makes 4 servings

Per serving: 248 calories, 5 g protein, 46 g carbohydrates, 6 g total fat, 3 g saturated fat, 3 g fiber, 60 mg sodium

Berries are super sources of antioxidants, so this is an indulgence you can feel good about.

# Banana Ice Cream with Chocolate Sauce

¾ cup sugar

7 tablespoons unsweetened cocoa powder

1 teaspoon cornstarch

½ cup fat-free milk

4 overripe bananas, frozen

IN a medium saucepan, whisk together the sugar, cocoa, cornstarch, and ¼ cup of the milk to form a paste. Stir in the remaining ¼ cup milk. Cook and stir over medium heat for 5 minutes, or until smooth and slightly thickened. Let cool for 5 minutes.

CUT the bananas into 1" pieces. Place in a blender or food processor. Blend or process for about 2 minutes, scraping down the sides of the bowl as needed, or until smooth. Divide among 4 serving dishes. Top with the chocolate sauce.

------

Total time: 20 minutes ✳ Makes 4 servings

Per serving: 285 calories, 4 g protein, 72 g carbohydrates, 6 g total fat, 2 g saturated fat, 1 g fiber, 16 mg sodium

When bananas get too ripe, peel them and freeze in a resealable plastic bag to save for this potassium-rich yet decadent dessert.

# Pomegranate Granita

3 **cups pomegranate juice**

½ **cup agave nectar**

6 **leaves fresh mint (optional)**

**IN** a medium bowl, combine the pomegranate juice and agave nectar. Stir until the nectar is dissolved. Pour into a 13" × 9" freezerproof dish. Place in the freezer for 1 hour.

**WITH** a fork, break up the mixture by raking across the surface to make fine-grained fragments. Return to the freezer. Repeat every 30 minutes for about 3 hours, or until the mixture is frozen in fine chips. Scoop into dessert dishes and garnish with mint (if using).

Total time: 4 hours 10 minutes **✱** Makes 6 servings

Per serving: 152 calories, 1 g protein, 39 g carbohydrates, 0 g total fat, 0 g saturated fat, 0 g fiber, 15 mg sodium

When summer heat and humidity soar, relieve the suffering with this refreshing Italian-style ice.

# Mango Sorbet, Almond, and Strawberry Delight

1 pint mango sorbet, slightly softened

1½ cups light vanilla ice cream, slightly softened

⅔ cup coarsely crushed almond biscotti (about 3 ounces)

¼ cup chopped slivered almonds, toasted (see note page 98)

2 teaspoons orange extract

1 pint strawberries, sliced

2 tablespoons honey

1 tablespoon finely sliced fresh mint leaves

LINE 6 custard cups or ramekins with a 3"-wide strip of waxed paper that extends several inches above opposite sides. Divide half of the sorbet among the ramekins and smooth to an even layer. Freeze for 15 minutes, or until firm. Keep the remaining sorbet in the coldest part of the refrigerator so it doesn't completely melt.

IN a medium bowl, combine the ice cream, biscotti, almonds, and orange extract. Divide among the custard cups. Smooth the tops and freeze for 15 minutes, or until firm.

MEANWHILE, in a medium bowl, stir together the strawberries, honey, and mint. Refrigerate.

DIVIDE the remaining sorbet among the custard cups. Smooth the tops and freeze for about 15 minutes, or until firm.

INVERT the cups onto 6 dessert plates. Gently pull on the waxed paper to loosen and unmold. Remove the waxed paper. Spoon the berries onto the plates.

-------------------------------------------------

Total time: 1 hour  ✱  Makes 6 servings

Per serving: 256 calories, 3 g protein, 52 g carbohydrates, 7 g total fat, 2 g saturated fat, 2 g fiber, 54 mg sodium

This dessert can be prepared up to 4 days ahead and stored in the freezer. Prepare the strawberry mixture just before serving. Let stand at room temperature for 15 minutes before serving.

# Menus for Special Times

**As you've learned** from perusing this edition of *Eat Up Slim Down! Annual Recipes 2012,* you can reach and maintain your goal weight while still living life to the fullest. Our weight-loss success subjects prove that mindful eating, regular moderate exercise, and good food choices combine to create the greatest cause for celebration: lasting good health. So go ahead and be the life of the party. Your healthy glow and the delectable dishes you share will inspire all around you.

To get you started, we've created more than a dozen good-time menus, featuring recipes from this book and simple nonrecipe sides that fit beautifully into your lifestyle. To keep you on track, each menu includes a one-serving nutritional analysis. The portion size for all the recipes is one serving. And because *Prevention* recommends that you limit saturated fat intake to 10 percent of total calories—about 17 grams per day for most women—and sodium intake to less than 2,300 milligrams, we've noted with an asterisk (*) which menus are slightly high in these nutrients, so you can remember to be mindful of your choices for the rest of the day.

From a Sunday Brunch to a Patio Cookout to a Book Club Buffet, the table is set for joyful times.

# Sunday Brunch

Mexican Egg-and-Spinach Bake,
page 62

Minted Honey-Lime Fruit Salad,
page 100

Coffee or tea

Per serving: 352 calories, 15 g protein,
50 g carbohydrates, 13 g total fat,
3 g saturated fat, 7 g fiber,
566 mg sodium

# Breakfast's in the Bag

Ham and Vegetable Omelet Wrap,
page 74

Pear Almond Muffins, page 93

Fat-free milk (1 cup)

Per serving: 395 calories, 28 g protein,
50 g carbohydrates, 11 g total fat,
3 g saturated fat, 6 g fiber,
773 mg sodium

# Pack-a-Picnic Lunch

Tuna Antipasto Sandwiches, page 115

Seedless red grapes (1 cup)

Iced tea with lemon (unsweetened)

Per serving: 458 calories, 30 g protein,
67 g carbohydrates, 11 g total fat,
2 g saturated fat, 15 g fiber,
765 mg sodium

# Lunch for a Bunch

Warm Rosemary Beef Salad with
Gorgonzola, page 127

Rolled Biscuits, page 95

Sparkling water with lime

Per serving: 330 calories, 31 g protein,
17 g carbohydrates, 15 g total fat,
5 g saturated fat, 4 g fiber,
568 mg sodium

# Autumn Feast

Honey-Roasted Turkey Breast,
page 213

Savory Bread Stuffing, page 249

Sweet-and-Sour Brussels Sprouts,
page 243

Perfect Pumpkin Pie, page 294

Per serving: 503 calories, 46 g protein,
66 g carbohydrates, 6 g total fat,
1 g saturated fat, 8 g fiber,
612 mg sodium

# Soup for Supper

Southwest Turkey Soup, page 142

1 corn tortilla, heated

2 ounces reduced-fat Cheddar cheese,
cubed

Lemon Gelatin Whip, page 310

Per serving: 412 calories, 49 g protein,
24 g carbohydrates, 15 g total fat,
7 g saturated fat, 3 g fiber,
920 mg sodium

# Thai for Supper

Thai Stir-Fried Shrimp and Crispy
Vegetables, page 228

½ cup cooked instant brown rice

½ cup diced mango

Per serving: 469 calories, 39 g protein,
62 g carbohydrates, 9 g total fat,
1 g saturated fat, 7 g fiber,
563 mg sodium

# Patio Cookout

Pineapple-Glazed Pork Chops,
page 199

Cajun Sweet Potato Fries, page 240

1 cup mixed greens drizzled with
balsamic vinegar

Per serving: 364 calories, 35 g protein,
35 g carbohydrates, 8 g total fat,
2 g saturated fat, 5 g fiber,
590 mg sodium

✱

# A Cozy Supper

Braised Chicken and Cannellini Beans, page 205

1 slice whole grain Italian bread

1 clementine

Per serving: 475 calories, 35 g protein, 68 g carbohydrates, 9 g total fat, 1 g saturated fat, 16 g fiber, 631 mg sodium

✱

# Easy Italian Buffet

Zucchini and Spinach Lasagna, page 234

Marinated Chickpea Salad, page 134

Pomegranate Granita, page 320

Per serving: 470 calories, 18 g protein, 71 g carbohydrates, 13 g total fat, 4 g saturated fat, 4 g fiber, 851 mg sodium*

# Down-by-the-Sea Dinner

Portuguese Mussel Stew, page 227

Zucchini and Bean Salad, page 258

Per serving: 405 calories, 26 g protein,
31 g carbohydrates, 18 g total fat,
3 g saturated fat, 7 g fiber,
882 mg sodium*

# Let's Celebrate

Chinese Beef and Pasta Skillet Supper,
page 191

Roasted Broccoli with Orange,
page 247

Chocolate-Nut Torte with Ganache,
page 286

Per serving: 674 calories, 39 g protein,
65 g carbohydrates, 32 g total fat,
9 g saturated fat*, 10 g fiber,
699 mg sodium

# Book Club Buffet

Greek Chicken Meatballs in Lettuce Cups, page 157

Asparagus with Smoked Turkey Ribbons, page 161

Citrus Cookies, page 177

1 serving Minted Honey-Lime Fruit Salad, page 100

Per serving: 377 calories, 32 g protein, 39 g carbohydrates, 12 g total fat, 2 g saturated fat, 5 g fiber, 255 mg sodium

# A Spring Splurge

Spiced Orange Roast Leg of Lamb, page 202

3 baby red potatoes, steamed, sprinkled with minced chives

2 ounces asparagus spears, steamed, drizzled with lemon juice

1 Strawberry Cream Cloud, page 311

Per serving: 487 calories, 41 g protein, 42 g carbohydrates, 17 g total fat, 8 g saturated fat, 4 g fiber, 368 mg sodium

# Calorie & Nutrient Counter

**There's no better way** to upset your weight-loss goals than to not have the right foods to eat on hand. But with the sheer number of foods available in the average market, making the best choices isn't always as easy as it would seem. That's why we've gathered all the nutrition facts you need to consider in the following list of common foods. Use this handy chart as your guide to determine which of your favorite fresh fruits and vegetables offer the most fiber, learn which cuts of meat are leaner than others, and make sure you're not overloading on too much sodium or saturated fat in your cheese choices.

You can also use this chart to get a grasp on exactly what you're eating so you can find out where the bulk of your calories comes from. Then you can make simple substitutions that shave off calories without sacrificing taste or satisfaction. For example, consider trading a handful of pretzels for 3 cups of air-popped popcorn sprinkled with 1 tablespoon of grated Parmesan cheese—you'll save about 115 calories and enjoy loads more flavor while tripling your portion size. Need some more motivation? Just remember that when you're guessing how many calories you can eat, being off by just 100 calories a day can keep you 6 to 10 pounds overweight.

# ✱ BEANS AND LEGUMES

| FOOD ITEM | SERVING SIZE | CALORIES | PROTEIN (G) |
|---|---|---|---|
| Baked beans | ½ cup | 140 | 6 |
| Baked beans, vegetarian | ⅓ cup | 79 | 4 |
| Bean sprouts (mung beans) | ½ cup | 13 | 1 |
| Black beans, cooked with salt | ½ cup | 114 | 8 |
| Black-eyed peas (cowpeas), cooked with salt | ½ cup | 99 | 7 |
| Butter beans (lima), cooked with salt | ½ cup | 105 | 6 |
| Cannellini beans, cooked without salt | ½ cup | 100 | 6 |
| Chickpeas (garbanzo beans), cooked with salt | ½ cup | 134 | 7 |
| Edamame (immature green soybeans), frozen, prepared | ½ cup | 95 | 8 |
| Edamame, out of shell, cooked without salt | ½ cup | 100 | 10 |
| Falafel, cooked | 2¼" patty | 57 | 2 |
| French beans, cooked with salt | ½ cup | 114 | 6 |
| Hummus | ⅛ cup | 54 | 1 |
| Kidney beans, red, cooked with salt | ½ cup | 112 | 8 |
| Lentils, brown, cooked with salt | ½ cup | 115 | 9 |
| Navy beans, cooked with salt | ½ cup | 127 | 7 |
| Pinto beans, cooked with salt | ½ cup | 122 | 8 |
| Refried beans, canned | ½ cup | 118 | 7 |
| Refried beans, fat-free | ½ cup | 130 | 6 |
| Refried beans, vegetarian | ½ cup | 100 | 6 |
| Soybeans, dry-roasted, salted | ¼ cup | 194 | 17 |
| White beans, small, cooked with salt | ½ cup | 127 | 8 |

| CARB (G) | FIBER (G) | SUGAR (G) | FAT (G) | SAT FAT (G) | SODIUM (MG) |
|---|---|---|---|---|---|
| 29 | 5 | 12 | 1 | 0 | 550 |
| 18 | 3 | 7 | 1 | 0 | 288 |
| 3 | 1 | 2 | 0 | 0 | 6 |
| 20 | 8 | 0 | 1 | 0 | 204 |
| 18 | 6 | 3 | 1 | 0 | 205 |
| 20 | 5 | 1 | 0 | 0 | 215 |
| 17 | 5 | 1 | 1 | 0 | 40 |
| 22 | 6 | 4 | 2 | 0 | 199 |
| 8 | 4 | 2 | 4 | 0 | 5 |
| 9 | 1 | 2 | 3 | 0 | 70 |
| 5 | 0 | 0 | 3 | 0 | 50 |
| 21 | 8 | 0 | 1 | 0 | 214 |
| 6 | 1 | 0 | 3 | 0 | 74 |
| 20 | 7 | 0 | 0 | 0 | 211 |
| 20 | 8 | 2 | 0 | 0 | 236 |
| 24 | 10 | 0 | 1 | 0 | 216 |
| 22 | 8 | 0 | 1 | 0 | 203 |
| 20 | 7 | 0 | 2 | 1 | 379 |
| 18 | 6 | 1 | 0 | 0 | 580 |
| 17 | 6 | 2 | 1 | 0 | 560 |
| 14 | 4 | 0 | 9 | 1 | 70 |
| 23 | 9 | 0 | 1 | 0 | 213 |

*(continued)*

# ✳ CHEESE

| FOOD ITEM | SERVING SIZE | CALORIES | PROTEIN (G) |
|---|---|---|---|
| American, pasteurized process, fat-free | 1" cube | 24 | 4 |
| American, pasteurized process, low-fat | 1" cube | 32 | 4 |
| American cheese food | 1 oz | 93 | 6 |
| American cheese food, low-fat | 1" cube | 32 | 4 |
| Blue, crumbled | 1 Tbsp | 30 | 2 |
| Brie | 1" cube | 57 | 4 |
| Cheddar | 1" cube | 69 | 4 |
| Cheddar, fat-free | 1" cube | 40 | 8 |
| Cheddar, low-fat | 1" cube | 30 | 4 |
| Cottage cheese, fat-free, large-curd, dry | ½ cup | 96 | 20 |
| Cottage cheese, low-fat 1% | 4 oz | 81 | 14 |
| Cottage cheese, low-fat 2% | ¼ cup | 51 | 8 |
| Cream cheese | 2 Tbsp | 101 | 2 |
| Cream cheese, fat-free | 2 Tbsp | 28 | 4 |
| Cream cheese, low-fat | 2 Tbsp | 69 | 3 |
| Feta | 1" cube | 45 | 2 |
| Monterey Jack, fat-free | 1" cube | 40 | 8 |
| Monterey Jack, low-fat | 1" cube | 53 | 5 |
| Mozzarella, fat-free, shredded | ¼ oz | 42 | 9 |
| Mozzarella, low-sodium | 1" cube | 50 | 5 |
| Mozzarella, part-skim, low-moisture | 1 oz | 86 | 7 |
| Mozzarella, string | 1 (1 oz) | 80 | 8 |
| Muenster | 1" cube | 66 | 4 |
| Muenster, low-fat | 1" cube | 49 | 4 |
| Parmesan, grated | 2 Tbsp | 43 | 4 |
| Parmesan, hard | 1" cube | 40 | 4 |

| CARB (G) | FIBER (G) | SUGAR (G) | FAT (G) | SAT FAT (G) | SODIUM (MG) |
|---|---|---|---|---|---|
| 2 | 0 | 2 | 0 | 0 | 244 |
| 1 | 0 | 0 | 1 | 1 | 257 |
| 2 | 0 | 2 | 7 | 4 | 452 |
| 1 | 0 | 0 | 1 | 1 | 257 |
| 0 | 0 | 0 | 3 | 1.5 | 118 |
| 0 | 0 | 0 | 5 | 3 | 107 |
| 0 | 0 | 0 | 6 | 4 | 106 |
| 1 | 0 | 1 | 0 | 0 | 220 |
| 0 | 0 | 0 | 1 | 1 | 106 |
| 2 | 0 | 2 | 0 | 0 | 15 |
| 3 | 0 | 3 | 1 | 1 | 459 |
| 2 | 0 | 0 | 1 | 1 | 229 |
| 1 | 0 | 0 | 10 | 6 | 86 |
| 2 | 0 | 0 | 0 | 0 | 158 |
| 2 | 0 | 0 | 5 | 3 | 89 |
| 1 | 0 | 1 | 4 | 3 | 190 |
| 1 | 0 | 1 | 0 | 0 | 220 |
| 0 | 0 | 0 | 4 | 2 | 96 |
| 1 | 1 | 0 | 0 | 0 | 210 |
| 1 | 0 | 0 | 3 | 2 | 3 |
| 1 | 0 | 0 | 6 | 4 | 150 |
| 1 | 0 | 0 | 6 | 3 | 240 |
| 0 | 0 | 0 | 5 | 3 | 113 |
| 1 | 0 | 1 | 3 | 2 | 108 |
| 0 | 0 | 0 | 3 | 2 | 153 |
| 0 | 0 | 0 | 3 | 2 | 165 |

(continued)

## ✳ CHEESE (cont.)

| FOOD ITEM | SERVING SIZE | CALORIES | PROTEIN (G) |
|---|---|---|---|
| Provolone | 1" cube | 60 | 4 |
| Ricotta | ¼ cup | 107 | 7 |
| Ricotta, low-fat | ¼ cup | 85 | 7 |
| Swiss | 1" cube | 57 | 4 |
| Swiss, low-fat | 1" cube | 27 | 4 |
| Swiss, low-fat, singles | 1 slice | 50 | 8 |

## ✳ OTHER DAIRY

| FOOD ITEM | SERVING SIZE | CALORIES | PROTEIN (G) |
|---|---|---|---|
| Sour cream | 1 Tbsp | 31 | 0 |
| Yogurt, banana, low-fat | 4 oz | 120 | 5 |
| Yogurt, blueberry–French vanilla, low-fat | 4 oz | 120 | 5 |
| Yogurt, coffee, fat-free | 4 oz | 103 | 6 |
| Yogurt, plain, fat-free | 4 oz | 63 | 6 |
| Yogurt, plain, low-fat | 4 oz | 71 | 6 |
| Yogurt, plain, whole-milk | 4 oz | 69 | 4 |
| Yogurt, strawberry, fat-free, Breyer's | 4 oz | 62 | 4 |
| Yogurt, strawberry, low-fat, Breyer's | 4 oz | 109 | 4 |
| Yogurt, vanilla, low-fat | 4 oz | 96 | 6 |

| CARB (G) | FIBER (G) | SUGAR (G) | FAT (G) | SAT FAT (G) | SODIUM (MG) |
|----------|-----------|-----------|---------|-------------|-------------|
| 0 | 0 | 0 | 5 | 3 | 149 |
| 2 | 0 | 0 | 8 | 5 | 52 |
| 3 | 0 | 0 | 5 | 3 | 77 |
| 1 | 0 | 0 | 4 | 3 | 29 |
| 1 | 0 | 0 | 1 | 1 | 39 |
| 1 | 0 | 0 | 1 | 1 | 73 |

| CARB (G) | FIBER (G) | SUGAR (G) | FAT (G) | SAT FAT (G) | SODIUM (MG) |
|----------|-----------|-----------|---------|-------------|-------------|
| 1 | 0 | 0 | 3 | 2 | 8 |
| 21 | 0 | 18 | 2 | 2 | 60 |
| 24 | 0 | 21 | 1 | 0 | 70 |
| 20 | 0 | 20 | 0 | 0 | 78 |
| 9 | 0 | 9 | 0 | 0 | 87 |
| 8 | 0 | 8 | 2 | 1 | 79 |
| 5 | 0 | 5 | 4 | 2 | 52 |
| 11 | 0 | 9 | 0 | 0 | 51 |
| 21 | 0 | 20 | 1 | 1 | 59 |
| 16 | 0 | 16 | 1 | 1 | 75 |

*(continued)*

# ✳ EGGS

| FOOD ITEM | SERVING SIZE | CALORIES | PROTEIN (G) |
|---|---|---|---|
| Egg, hard-cooked | 1 large | 78 | 6 |
| Egg, poached | 1 large | 71 | 6 |
| Egg, scrambled | 1 large | 102 | 7 |
| Egg white, cooked | 1 large | 17 | 4 |
| Egg white, Egg Beaters | ¼ cup | 30 | 6 |

# ✳ FATS AND OILS

| FOOD ITEM | SERVING SIZE | CALORIES | PROTEIN (G) |
|---|---|---|---|
| Butter, without salt | 1 tsp | 34 | 0 |
| Butter, with salt | 1 tsp | 34 | 0 |
| Butter-margarine blend, stick, without salt | 1 tsp | 33 | 0 |
| Flaxseed oil | 1 tsp | 40 | 0 |
| Margarine, hard, corn and soybean oils | 1 tsp | 33 | 0 |
| Margarine, hard, corn oil | 1 tsp | 34 | 0 |
| Margarine, hard, soybean oil | 1 tsp | 34 | 0 |
| Margarine, regular, without salt | 1 tsp | 34 | 0 |
| Margarine, regular, with salt | 1 tsp | 34 | 0 |
| Oil, canola | 1 tsp | 40 | 0 |
| Oil, olive | 1 tsp | 40 | 0 |
| Oil, safflower | 1 tsp | 40 | 0 |
| Oil, sesame | 1 tsp | 40 | 0 |
| Oil, walnut | 1 tsp | 40 | 0 |

| CARB (G) | FIBER (G) | SUGAR (G) | FAT (G) | SAT FAT (G) | SODIUM (MG) |
|---|---|---|---|---|---|
| 1 | 0 | 1 | 5 | 2 | 62 |
| 0 | 0 | 0 | 5 | 2 | 147 |
| 1 | 0 | 1 | 7 | 2 | 171 |
| 0 | 0 | 0 | 0 | 0 | 55 |
| 1 | 0 | 0 | 0 | 0 | 115 |

| CARB (G) | FIBER (G) | SUGAR (G) | FAT (G) | SAT FAT (G) | SODIUM (MG) |
|---|---|---|---|---|---|
| 0 | 0 | 0 | 4 | 2 | 1 |
| 0 | 0 | 0 | 4 | 2 | 27 |
| 0 | 0 | 0 | 4 | 1 | 1 |
| 0 | 0 | 0 | 5 | 0 | 0 |
| 0 | 0 | 0 | 4 | 1 | 30 |
| 0 | 0 | 0 | 4 | 1 | 44 |
| 0 | 0 | 0 | 4 | 1 | 44 |
| 0 | 0 | 0 | 4 | 1 | 0 |
| 0 | 0 | 0 | 4 | 1 | 44 |
| 0 | 0 | 0 | 5 | 0 | 0 |
| 0 | 0 | 0 | 5 | 1 | 0 |
| 0 | 0 | 0 | 5 | 0 | 0 |
| 0 | 0 | 0 | 5 | 1 | 0 |
| 0 | 0 | 0 | 5 | 0 | 0 |

*(continued)*

**FISH**

| FOOD ITEM | SERVING SIZE | CALORIES | PROTEIN (G) |
|---|---|---|---|
| Cod, Atlantic, baked | 3 oz | 89 | 19 |
| Flounder, baked | 3 oz | 99 | 21 |
| Grouper, baked | 3 oz | 100 | 21 |
| Halibut, Atlantic and Pacific, baked | 3 oz | 119 | 23 |
| Mahi mahi, baked | 3 oz | 93 | 20 |
| Salmon, Coho, wild, baked | 3 oz | 118 | 20 |
| Salmon, pink, canned, drained | 3 oz | 116 | 20 |
| Swordfish, baked | 3 oz | 132 | 22 |
| Tilapia, baked or broiled | 3 oz | 109 | 22 |
| Tuna, bluefin, baked | 3 oz | 156 | 25 |
| Tuna, StarKist Chunk Light, canned in water, drained | 2 oz | 70 | 15 |
| Tuna, white, canned in water, drained | 3 oz | 109 | 20 |
| Tuna, yellowfin, baked | 3 oz | 118 | 25 |

**FRUIT**

| FOOD ITEM | SERVING SIZE | CALORIES | PROTEIN (G) |
|---|---|---|---|
| Apple | 1 medium (2¾") | 72 | 0 |
| Apricot | 1 | 17 | 0 |
| Avocado | ¼ cup | 58 | 1 |
| Banana | 1 large (8") | 121 | 1 |
| Blackberries | 1 cup | 62 | 2 |
| Blueberries | ½ cup | 42 | 1 |
| Cantaloupe, wedged | ⅛ medium | 23 | 1 |
| Cranberries | 1 cup | 44 | 0 |
| Grapefruit, pink, red, or white | ½ medium | 41 | 1 |

| CARB (G) | FIBER (G) | SUGAR (G) | FAT (G) | SAT FAT (G) | SODIUM (MG) |
|---|---|---|---|---|---|
| 0 | 0 | 0 | 1 | 0 | 66 |
| 0 | 0 | 0 | 1 | 0 | 89 |
| 0 | 0 | 0 | 1 | 0 | 45 |
| 0 | 0 | 0 | 3 | 0 | 59 |
| 0 | 0 | 0 | 1 | 0 | 96 |
| 0 | 0 | 0 | 4 | 1 | 49 |
| 0 | 0 | 0 | 4 | 1 | 339 |
| 0 | 0 | 0 | 4 | 1 | 98 |
| 0 | 0 | 0 | 2 | 1 | 48 |
| 0 | 0 | 0 | 5 | 1 | 42 |
| 0 | 0 | 0 | 0 | 0 | 230 |
| 0 | 0 | 0 | 3 | 1 | 320 |
| 0 | 0 | 0 | 1 | 0 | 40 |

| CARB (G) | FIBER (G) | SUGAR (G) | FAT (G) | SAT FAT (G) | SODIUM (MG) |
|---|---|---|---|---|---|
| 19 | 3 | 14 | 0 | 0 | 1 |
| 4 | 1 | 3 | 0 | 0 | 0 |
| 3 | 2 | 0 | 5 | 1 | 3 |
| 31 | 4 | 17 | 0 | 0 | 1 |
| 14 | 8 | 7 | 1 | 0 | 1 |
| 11 | 2 | 7 | 0 | 0 | 1 |
| 6 | 1 | 5 | 0 | 0 | 11 |
| 12 | 4 | 4 | 0 | 0 | 2 |
| 10 | 1 | 9 | 0 | 0 | 0 |

*(continued)*

## ✳ FRUIT (cont.)

| FOOD ITEM | SERVING SIZE | CALORIES | PROTEIN (G) |
|---|---|---|---|
| Grapes, green or red | ½ cup | 52 | 1 |
| Lemon | 1 medium (2⅛") | 17 | 1 |
| Nectarine | 1 medium (2¾") | 69 | 2 |
| Orange | 1 large (3 1/16") | 86 | 2 |
| Peach | 1 medium | 58 | 1 |
| Pear | ½ medium | 52 | 0 |
| Pineapple | ¼ | 57 | 1 |
| Plum | 1 (2⅛") | 30 | 0 |
| Raspberries, red | ¾ cup | 48 | 1 |
| Strawberry | 1 medium | 4 | 0 |
| Watermelon, sliced | 1 wedge (1/16 melon) | 86 | 2 |

## ✳ GRAINS AND RICE

| FOOD ITEM | SERVING SIZE | CALORIES | PROTEIN (G) |
|---|---|---|---|
| Couscous, cooked | ⅓ cup | 59 | 2 |
| Oat bran, cooked | ⅓ cup | 29 | 2 |
| Oats, rolled, dry | 2 Tbsp | 37 | 1 |
| Quinoa, dry | 2 Tbsp | 79 | 3 |
| Rice, brown, long-grain, cooked | ¼ cup | 54 | 1 |
| Rice, brown, medium-grain, cooked | ¼ cup | 55 | 1 |
| Rice, brown, short-grain, dry | 1½ Tbsp | 66 | 1 |
| Rice, white, long-grain, cooked | ¼ cup | 51 | 1 |

| CARB (G) | FIBER (G) | SUGAR (G) | FAT (G) | SAT FAT (G) | SODIUM (MG) |
|---|---|---|---|---|---|
| 14 | 1 | 12 | 0 | 0 | 2 |
| 5 | 2 | 1 | 0 | 0 | 1 |
| 16 | 3 | 12 | 1 | 0 | 0 |
| 22 | 4 | 17 | 0 | 0 | 0 |
| 14 | 2 | 13 | 0 | 0 | 0 |
| 14 | 3 | 9 | 0 | 0 | 1 |
| 15 | 2 | 11 | 0 | 0 | 1 |
| 8 | 1 | 7 | 0 | 0 | 0 |
| 11 | 6 | 4 | 1 | 0 | 1 |
| 1 | 0 | 1 | 0 | 0 | 2 |
| 22 | 1 | 18 | 0 | 0 | 3 |

| CARB (G) | FIBER (G) | SUGAR (G) | FAT (G) | SAT FAT (G) | SODIUM (MG) |
|---|---|---|---|---|---|
| 12 | 1 | 0 | 0 | 0 | 3 |
| 8 | 2 | 0 | 1 | 0 | 1 |
| 7 | 1 | 0 | 1 | 0 | 0 |
| 15 | 1 | 0 | 1 | 0 | 4 |
| 11 | 1 | 0 | 1 | 0 | 2 |
| 11 | 1 | 0 | 0 | 0 | 0 |
| 15 | 1 | 0 | 1 | 0 | 2 |
| 11 | 0 | 0 | 0 | 0 | 0 |

*(continued)*

## ✻ GRAINS AND RICE *(cont.)*

| FOOD ITEM | SERVING SIZE | CALORIES | PROTEIN (G) |
|---|---|---|---|
| Rice, whole grain, brown, Uncle Ben's 10-minute, dry | ¼ cup | 170 | 1 |
| Rice, wild, cooked | ⅓ cup | 55 | 2 |

## ✻ MEATS

| FOOD ITEM | SERVING SIZE | CALORIES | PROTEIN (G) |
|---|---|---|---|
| BEEF | | | |
| Bottom round, all lean, boneless, roasted | 3 oz | 144 | 24 |
| Filet mignon, lean, broiled | 3 oz | 164 | 24 |
| Flank steak, lean, braised | 3 oz | 201 | 24 |
| Ground, extra lean (5% fat), raw | 4 oz | 155 | 24 |
| Ground patty, 10% fat, raw | 4 oz | 199 | 23 |
| Hot dog, beef, fat-free | 1 frank | 62 | 7 |
| Roast beef, lunchmeat, medium-rare | 1 oz | 30 | 6 |
| Steak, top sirloin, lean, broiled | 3 oz | 160 | 26 |
| PORK | | | |
| Bacon, medium slice, cooked | 1 slice | 43 | 3 |
| Canadian bacon, grilled | 1 slice | 43 | 6 |
| Chop, center, lean, with bone, braised | 3 oz | 172 | 25 |
| Chop, sirloin, lean, with bone, braised | 1 chop | 142 | 19 |
| Ground, cooked | 3 oz | 252 | 22 |
| Ham, low-sodium, 96% fat-free, roasted, boneless | 1 oz | 47 | 6 |
| Hot dog, pork | 1 frank | 204 | 10 |
| Ribs, country-style, lean, braised | 3 oz | 199 | 22 |

| CARB (G) | FIBER (G) | SUGAR (G) | FAT (G) | SAT FAT (G) | SODIUM (MG) |
|---|---|---|---|---|---|
| 35 | 2 | 0 | 2 | 0 | 0 |
| 12 | 1 | 0 | 0 | 0 | 2 |

| CARB (G) | FIBER (G) | SUGAR (G) | FAT (G) | SAT FAT (G) | SODIUM (MG) |
|---|---|---|---|---|---|
| 0 | 0 | 0 | 5 | 2 | 32 |
| 0 | 0 | 0 | 7 | 3 | 50 |
| 0 | 0 | 0 | 11 | 5 | 61 |
| 0 | 0 | 0 | 6 | 3 | 75 |
| 0 | 0 | 0 | 11 | 5 | 75 |
| 3 | 0 | 0 | 1 | 0 | 455 |
| 1 | 0 | 1 | 1 | 1 | 235 |
| 0 | 0 | 0 | 6 | 2 | 54 |
| 0 | 0 | 0 | 3 | 1 | 185 |
| 0 | 0 | 0 | 2 | 1 | 363 |
| 0 | 0 | 0 | 7 | 3 | 53 |
| 0 | 0 | 0 | 6 | 2 | 38 |
| 0 | 0 | 0 | 18 | 7 | 62 |
| 0 | 0 | 0 | 2 | 1 | 275 |
| 0 | 0 | 0 | 18 | 7 | 620 |
| 0 | 0 | 0 | 12 | 4 | 54 |

*(continued)*

## ❋ MEATS *(cont.)*

| FOOD ITEM | SERVING SIZE | CALORIES | PROTEIN (G) |
|---|---|---|---|
| Sausage, pork, cooked | 1 oz (1 each) | 82 | 4 |
| Tenderloin, lean, roasted | 3 oz | 139 | 24 |
| VEAL | | | |
| Breast, lean, boneless, braised | 3 oz | 185 | 26 |
| Ground, broiled | 3 oz | 146 | 21 |
| Loin, lean, roasted | 3 oz | 149 | 22 |

## ❋ NUTS, SEEDS, AND BUTTERS

| FOOD ITEM | SERVING SIZE | CALORIES | PROTEIN (G) |
|---|---|---|---|
| Almond butter, plain, with salt | 1 Tbsp | 101 | 2 |
| Almonds, dry-roasted, with salt | ½ oz (11 nuts) | 85 | 3 |
| Almonds, natural, sliced | ½ oz | 82 | 3 |
| Brazil nuts, dried | 1 nut | 33 | 1 |
| Brazil nuts, dried | ½ oz (3 nuts) | 93 | 2 |
| Cashew butter, plain, with salt | 1 Tbsp | 94 | 3 |
| Cashew nuts, dry-roasted, with salt | ½ oz | 81 | 2 |
| Cashew nuts, raw | ½ oz | 78 | 3 |
| Flaxseed, ground | 1 Tbsp | 37 | 1 |
| Macadamia nuts, dry-roasted, with salt | ½ oz (5–6 nuts) | 101 | 1 |
| Mixed nuts, dry-roasted, with peanuts, with salt | ½ oz | 84 | 2 |
| Peanut butter, creamy, with salt | 1 Tbsp | 94 | 4 |
| Peanut butter, crunchy, with salt | 1 Tbsp | 95 | 4 |
| Peanut butter, natural | 1 Tbsp | 100 | 4 |
| Peanut butter, reduced-fat, with salt | 1 Tbsp | 83 | 4 |

| CARB (G) | FIBER (G) | SUGAR (G) | FAT (G) | SAT FAT (G) | SODIUM (MG) |
|---|---|---|---|---|---|
| 0 | 0 | 0 | 8 | 3 | 200 |
| 0 | 0 | 0 | 4 | 1 | 48 |
| 0 | 0 | 0 | 8 | 3 | 58 |
| 0 | 0 | 0 | 6 | 3 | 71 |
| 0 | 0 | 0 | 6 | 2 | 82 |

| CARB (G) | FIBER (G) | SUGAR (G) | FAT (G) | SAT FAT (G) | SODIUM (MG) |
|---|---|---|---|---|---|
| 3 | 1 | 1 | 9 | 1 | 72 |
| 3 | 2 | 1 | 7 | 1 | 48 |
| 3 | 2 | 1 | 7 | 1 | 0 |
| 1 | 0 | 0 | 3 | 1 | 0 |
| 2 | 1 | 0 | 9 | 2 | 0 |
| 4 | 0 | 1 | 8 | 2 | 98 |
| 5 | 0 | 1 | 7 | 1 | 91 |
| 4 | 1 | 1 | 6 | 1 | 2 |
| 2 | 2 | 0 | 3 | 0 | 2 |
| 2 | 1 | 1 | 11 | 2 | 38 |
| 4 | 1 | 1 | 7 | 1 | 95 |
| 3 | 1 | 1 | 8 | 2 | 73 |
| 3 | 1 | 1 | 8 | 1 | 78 |
| 4 | 1 | 1 | 8 | 1 | 60 |
| 6 | 1 | 1 | 5 | 1 | 86 |

*(continued)*

## ❋ NUTS, SEEDS, AND BUTTERS *(cont.)*

| FOOD ITEM | SERVING SIZE | CALORIES | PROTEIN (G) |
|---|---|---|---|
| Peanuts, dry-roasted, with salt | ½ oz | 83 | 3 |
| Peanuts, shelled, cooked, with salt | 1 Tbsp | 36 | 2 |
| Pecans, dried, chopped | ⅛ cup | 94 | 1 |
| Pecans, dried, halved | ⅛ cup | 86 | 1 |
| Pecans, dry-roasted, with salt | ½ oz | 101 | 1 |
| Pistachios, dry-roasted, with salt | ½ oz | 81 | 3 |
| Walnuts, dried, black | 1 Tbsp | 48 | 2 |
| Walnuts, dried, halved | ½ oz | 93 | 2 |
| Walnuts, English, ground | ⅛ cup | 65 | 2 |

## ❋ PASTA

| FOOD ITEM | SERVING SIZE | CALORIES | PROTEIN (G) |
|---|---|---|---|
| Angel hair, whole wheat, dry | 1 oz | 106 | 4 |
| Bow ties, semolina, dry | 1 oz | 103 | 4 |
| Fettuccine (tagliatelle), semolina, dry | 1 oz | 102 | 4 |
| Fettuccine (tagliatelle), spinach, dry | 1 oz | 98 | 4 |
| Lasagna, semolina, dry | 1 oz | 102 | 4 |
| Linguine, semolina, dry | 1 oz | 102 | 4 |

| CARB (G) | FIBER (G) | SUGAR (G) | FAT (G) | SAT FAT (G) | SODIUM (MG) |
|---|---|---|---|---|---|
| 3 | 1 | 1 | 7 | 1 | 115 |
| 2 | 1 | 0 | 3 | 0.5 | 84 |
| 2 | 1 | 1 | 10 | 0 | 0 |
| 2 | 1 | 1 | 9 | 1 | 0 |
| 2 | 1 | 1 | 11 | 1 | 54 |
| 4 | 2 | 1 | 7 | 1 | 57 |
| 1 | 1 | 0 | 5 | 0 | 0 |
| 2 | 1 | 0 | 9 | 0 | 0 |
| 1 | 1 | 0 | 7 | 1 | 0 |

| CARB (G) | FIBER (G) | SUGAR (G) | FAT (G) | SAT FAT (G) | SODIUM (MG) |
|---|---|---|---|---|---|
| 21 | 3 | 1 | 1 | 0 | 5 |
| 21 | 1 | 1 | 0 | 0 | 1 |
| 21 | 1 | 1 | 1 | 0 | 2 |
| 20 | 1 | 1 | 1 | 0 | 9 |
| 21 | 1 | 1 | 1 | 0 | 1 |
| 21 | 1 | 1 | 1 | 0 | 2 |

*(continued)*

## ✳ PASTA *(cont.)*

| FOOD ITEM | SERVING SIZE | CALORIES | PROTEIN (G) |
|---|---|---|---|
| Penne, semolina, dry | 1 oz | 106 | 4 |
| Penne, whole wheat, dry | 1 oz | 106 | 4 |
| Spaghetti, whole wheat, dry | 1 oz | 99 | 4 |

Note: For most pasta shapes, 1 ounce of dry pasta makes approximately ½ cup cooked.

## ✳ POULTRY

| FOOD ITEM | SERVING SIZE | CALORIES | PROTEIN (G) |
|---|---|---|---|
| CHICKEN | | | |
| Chicken, breast, boneless, without skin, roasted | ½ breast | 143 | 27 |
| Chicken, drumstick, without skin, roasted | 1 drumstick | 181 | 26 |
| Chicken, thigh, boneless, without skin, roasted | 1 thigh | 109 | 13 |
| Chicken frankfurter | 1 frank | 116 | 6 |
| Chicken lunchmeat, deli | 1 oz | 23 | 5 |
| TURKEY | | | |
| Turkey, breast, without skin, roasted | 3 oz | 133 | 25 |
| Turkey, dark meat, without skin, roasted | 3 oz | 135 | 25 |
| Turkey, dark meat, with skin, roasted | 3 oz | 144 | 24 |
| Turkey, ground, breast, 99% fat-free, cooked | 3 oz | 120 | 28 |
| Turkey, light meat, without skin, roasted | 3 oz | 134 | 25 |
| Turkey frankfurter | 1 frank | 102 | 6 |
| Turkey sausage, smoked, hot | 1 oz | 44 | 4 |

| CARB (G) | FIBER (G) | SUGAR (G) | FAT (G) | SAT FAT (G) | SODIUM (MG) |
|---|---|---|---|---|---|
| 22 | 1 | 1 | 1 | 0 | 3 |
| 21 | 3 | 1 | 1 | 0 | 5 |
| 21 | 4 | 1 | 1 | 0 | 2 |

| CARB (G) | FIBER (G) | SUGAR (G) | FAT (G) | SAT FAT (G) | SODIUM (MG) |
|---|---|---|---|---|---|
| 0 | 0 | 0 | 3 | 1 | 77 |
| 0 | 0 | 0 | 8 | 2 | 86 |
| 0 | 0 | 0 | 6 | 2 | 46 |
| 3 | 0 | 0 | 9 | 2 | 616 |
| 0 | 0 | 0 | 0 | 0 | 210 |
| 0 | 0 | 0 | 3 | 1 | 54 |
| 0 | 0 | 0 | 3 | 1 | 69 |
| 0 | 0 | 0 | 5 | 1 | 68 |
| 0 | 0 | 0 | 2 | 0 | 65 |
| 0 | 0 | 0 | 3 | 1 | 54 |
| 1 | 0 | 0 | 8 | 3 | 642 |
| 1 | 0 | 1 | 2 | 1 | 260 |

*(continued)*

## ✳ SEAFOOD

| FOOD ITEM | SERVING SIZE | CALORIES | PROTEIN (G) |
|---|---|---|---|
| Crab, Alaskan, king crab, steamed | 3 oz | 82 | 16 |
| Crab, baked or broiled | 3 oz | 117 | 16 |
| Crab, imitation (surimi) | 3 oz | 81 | 6 |
| Crab, sautéed | 3 oz | 117 | 16 |
| Lobster, Northern steamed | 3 oz | 83 | 17 |
| Shrimp, cooked | 3 oz | 84 | 17 |
| Shrimp, steamed | 1 large | 5 | 1 |

## ✳ VEGETABLES

| FOOD ITEM | SERVING SIZE | CALORIES | PROTEIN (G) |
|---|---|---|---|
| Alfalfa sprouts | ½ cup | 4 | 1 |
| Artichoke | 1 medium | 60 | 4 |
| Asparagus, cooked | 8 spears | 26 | 3 |
| Bell pepper, boiled | 1 cup | 38 | 1 |
| Bell pepper, chopped | 1 cup | 30 | 1 |
| Broccoli, florets, fresh | 1 cup | 56 | 6 |
| Brussels sprouts, raw | 1 cup | 38 | 3 |
| Cabbage, raw | 1 medium leaf | 6 | 0 |
| Carrot | 1 medium | 25 | 1 |
| Carrot, baby | 1 medium | 4 | 0 |
| Cauliflower | ¼ medium head | 36 | 3 |
| Celery | 1 medium stalk | 6 | 0 |
| Celery, chopped | 1 cup | 16 | 1 |

| CARB (G) | FIBER (G) | SUGAR (G) | FAT (G) | SAT FAT (G) | SODIUM (MG) |
|---|---|---|---|---|---|
| 0 | 0 | 0 | 1 | 0 | 911 |
| 0 | 0 | 0 | 6 | 1 | 270 |
| 13 | 0 | 5 | 0 | 0 | 715 |
| 0 | 0 | 0 | 5 | 1 | 270 |
| 1 | 0 | 0 | 1 | 0 | 323 |
| 0 | 0 | 0 | 1 | 0 | 190 |
| 0 | 0 | 0 | 0 | 0 | 12 |

| CARB (G) | FIBER (G) | SUGAR (G) | FAT (G) | SAT FAT (G) | SODIUM (MG) |
|---|---|---|---|---|---|
| 0 | 0 | 0 | 0 | 0 | 1 |
| 13 | 7 | 1 | 0 | 0 | 397 |
| 5 | 2 | 2 | 0 | 0 | 17 |
| 9 | 2 | 3 | 0 | 0 | 3 |
| 7 | 3 | 4 | 0 | 0 | 4 |
| 10 | 6 | 0 | 1 | 0 | 54 |
| 8 | 3 | 2 | 0 | 0 | 22 |
| 1 | 1 | 1 | 0 | 0 | 4 |
| 6 | 2 | 3 | 0 | 0 | 42 |
| 1 | 0 | 0 | 0 | 0 | 8 |
| 8 | 4 | 4 | 0 | 0 | 43 |
| 1 | 1 | 1 | 0 | 0 | 32 |
| 3 | 2 | 2 | 0 | 0 | 81 |

*(continued)*

## ✳ VEGETABLES *(cont.)*

| FOOD ITEM | SERVING SIZE | CALORIES | PROTEIN (G) |
|---|---|---|---|
| Cherry tomatoes, red | 1 cup | 27 | 1 |
| Corn, sweet white or yellow | ½ cup | 66 | 2 |
| Corn, sweet white or yellow | 1 large ear | 123 | 5 |
| Cucumber with peel, raw | 1 (8¼") | 45 | 2 |
| Garlic | 1 clove | 4 | 0 |
| Green beans, snap, raw | 1 cup | 34 | 2 |
| Green beans, with almonds, frozen, Green Giant | 1 cup | 91 | 3 |
| Lettuce, iceberg | 5 large leaves | 10 | 1 |
| Lettuce, romaine | 4 leaves | 19 | 1 |
| Mushrooms, brown Italian | 5 | 27 | 3 |
| Onion, green (scallions), tops and bulbs, chopped | ½ cup | 16 | 1 |
| Onion, red or yellow | 1 medium | 44 | 1 |
| Peas, green, raw | ½ cup | 59 | 4 |
| Peas, snow, whole, raw | ½ cup | 13 | 1 |
| Potato, baked, with skin, without salt | 1 medium | 161 | 4 |
| Sauerkraut, canned, low-sodium | 1 cup | 31 | 1 |
| Spinach | 3 oz | 20 | 2 |
| Spinach, cooked, without salt | 1 cup | 41 | 5 |
| Spinach, cooked, with salt | 1 cup | 41 | 5 |
| Squash, summer | 1 medium | 31 | 2 |
| Sweet potato, baked, with skin, without salt | 1 small | 54 | 1 |
| Tomato, red | 1 medium | 22 | 1 |
| Zucchini, with skin, raw | 1 medium | 31 | 2 |

Calorie &
Nutrient Counter

| CARB (G) | FIBER (G) | SUGAR (G) | FAT (G) | SAT FAT (G) | SODIUM (MG) |
|---|---|---|---|---|---|
| 6 | 2 | 4 | 0 | 0 | 7 |
| 15 | 2 | 2 | 1 | 0 | 12 |
| 27 | 4 | 5 | 2 | 0 | 21 |
| 11 | 2 | 5 | 0 | 0 | 6 |
| 1 | 0 | 0 | 0 | 0 | 1 |
| 8 | 4 | 2 | 0 | 0 | 7 |
| 8 | 3 | 3 | 5 | 0 | 144 |
| 2 | 1 | 1 | 0 | 0 | 8 |
| 4 | 2 | 1 | 0 | 0 | 9 |
| 4 | 1 | 2 | 0 | 0 | 6 |
| 4 | 1 | 1 | 0 | 0 | 8 |
| 10 | 2 | 5 | 0 | 0 | 4 |
| 10 | 4 | 4 | 0 | 0 | 4 |
| 2 | 1 | 1 | 0 | 0 | 1 |
| 37 | 4 | 2 | 0 | 0 | 17 |
| 6 | 4 | 3 | 0 | 0 | 437 |
| 3 | 2 | 0 | 0 | 0 | 67 |
| 7 | 4 | 1 | 0 | 0 | 126 |
| 7 | 4 | 1 | 0 | 0 | 551 |
| 7 | 2 | 4 | 0 | 0 | 4 |
| 12 | 2 | 4 | 0 | 0 | 22 |
| 5 | 1 | 3 | 0 | 0 | 0 |
| 7 | 2 | 3 | 0 | 0 | 20 |

# Photo Credits

Cover photography © Mitch Mandel/
Rodale Inc.
Recipe photography © Mitch Mandel/
Rodale Inc.; food styling by Diane
Vezza

All other photography © Mitch Mandel/
Rodale Inc., with the following
exceptions:
© Getty Images: pages x, 7, 10, 11, 18 (top),
19–21, 22 (right), 23, 26, 29 top (2) &
center (2), 31 (top left), 46, 49, 50, 58, 60,
104, 150, 188, 266, 322
© Shannon Greer: pages 2–5
© BananaStock: page 8
© David Tsay: page 9
© Erin Patrice O'Brien: page 12
© Hilmar: page 14
© Photodisc: page 17 (2nd from top)
© Thomas MacDonald/Rodale Inc.:
pages 17 (3rd from top), 22 (center), 28

© Image Source: page 17 (bottom)
© Gabrielle Revere: page 24
© Masterfile: page 29 (bottom)
© Corbis: page 30 (top left)
© Alamy: page 30 (bottom left)
© PhotoLibrary: pages 30 (top & bottom
right), 31 (top right), 31 (middle and
bottom left)
© James Baigrie: page 31 (middle right)
© Fotosearch: page 31 (bottom right)
© Travis Rathbone: page 32 (6)
© Timothy Hogan: page 33
© Gabriela Hasbun: page 34
© Charles Masters: page 36
© Levi Brown: pages 39, 40, 42, 51–53, 56
© Ngoc Ming Ngo: page 41
© John Kernick: page 43
© Thayer Allyson Gowdy: page 44
© Age Fotostock: page 55
Courtesy photos: pages 13, 25, 35, 45

# Index

Underscored page references indicate boxed text. **Boldfaced** page references indicate photographs.

# Conversion Chart

These equivalents have been slightly rounded to make measuring easier.

### VOLUME MEASUREMENTS

| U.S. | IMPERIAL | METRIC |
|------|----------|--------|
| ¼ tsp | – | 1 ml |
| ½ tsp | – | 2 ml |
| 1 tsp | – | 5 ml |
| 1 Tbsp | – | 15 ml |
| 2 Tbsp (1 oz) | 1 fl oz | 30 ml |
| ¼ cup (2 oz) | 2 fl oz | 60 ml |
| ⅓ cup (3 oz) | 3 fl oz | 80 ml |
| ½ cup (4 oz) | 4 fl oz | 120 ml |
| ⅔ cup (5 oz) | 5 fl oz | 160 ml |
| ¾ cup (6 oz) | 6 fl oz | 180 ml |
| 1 cup (8 oz) | 8 fl oz | 240 ml |

### WEIGHT MEASUREMENTS

| U.S. | METRIC |
|------|--------|
| 1 oz | 30 g |
| 2 oz | 60 g |
| 4 oz (¼ lb) | 115 g |
| 5 oz (⅓ lb) | 145 g |
| 6 oz | 170 g |
| 7 oz | 200 g |
| 8 oz (½ lb) | 230 g |
| 10 oz | 285 g |
| 12 oz (¾ lb) | 340 g |
| 14 oz | 400 g |
| 16 oz (1 lb) | 455 g |
| 2.2 lb | 1 kg |

### LENGTH MEASUREMENTS

| U.S. | METRIC |
|------|--------|
| ¼" | 0.6 cm |
| ½" | 1.25 cm |
| 1" | 2.5 cm |
| 2" | 5 cm |
| 4" | 11 cm |
| 6" | 15 cm |
| 8" | 20 cm |
| 10" | 25 cm |
| 12" (1') | 30 cm |

### PAN SIZES

| U.S. | METRIC |
|------|--------|
| 8" cake pan | 20 × 4 cm sandwich or cake tin |
| 9" cake pan | 23 × 3.5 cm sandwich or cake tin |
| 11" × 7" baking pan | 28 × 18 cm baking tin |
| 13" × 9" baking pan | 32.5 × 23 cm baking tin |
| 15" × 10" baking pan | 38 × 25.5 cm baking tin |
| | (Swiss roll tin) |
| 1½ qt baking dish | 1.5 liter baking dish |
| 2 qt baking dish | 2 liter baking dish |
| 2 qt rectangular baking dish | 30 × 19 cm baking dish |
| 9" pie plate | 22 × 4 or 23 × 4 cm pie plate |
| 7" or 8" springform pan | 18 or 20 cm springform or |
| | loose-bottom cake tin |
| 9" × 5" loaf pan | 23 × 13 cm or 2 lb narrow |
| | loaf tin or pâté tin |

### TEMPERATURES

| FAHRENHEIT | CENTIGRADE | GAS |
|------------|------------|-----|
| 140° | 60° | – |
| 160° | 70° | – |
| 180° | 80° | – |
| 225° | 105° | ¼ |
| 250° | 120° | ½ |
| 275° | 135° | 1 |
| 300° | 150° | 2 |
| 325° | 160° | 3 |
| 350° | 180° | 4 |
| 375° | 190° | 5 |
| 400° | 200° | 6 |
| 425° | 220° | 7 |
| 450° | 230° | 8 |
| 475° | 245° | 9 |
| 500° | 260° | – |